Logic: A Short and Simple Intr
James F. Crowley

TABLE OF CONTENTS

Introduction

In this brief survey of logic, we will consider five major topics:

1. TRADITIONAL LOGIC is the logic invented by Aristotle in ancient Athens about 350 B.C. and later developed by medieval philosophers. It concerns the relationships between terms.

2. SENTENTIAL LOGIC, or propositional logic, concerns the relationships between sentences. The sentential connectives are the foundations of modern symbolic logic, invented about the beginning of the 20th century by Gottlieb Frege in Germany and by Bertrand Russell and Alfred North Whitehead in Britain.

3. PREDICATE LOGIC allows us to integrate traditional Aristotelian logic with modern symbolic logic.

4. INDUCTIVE LOGIC is the logic of science.

5. INFORMAL LOGIC considers some of the most common fallacies we encounter in everyday life.

Logic can be divided into the following categories:

I. Formal
   A. Deductive
      1. Aristotelian
      2. Symbolic
         a. Sentential
         b. Predicate
   B. Inductive
II. Informal

Logic can be either formal or informal. Formal logic considers only the form of an argument into which you can place any words. Informal logic considers the content or words of an argument rather than just the form of an argument. Formal logic can be deductive or inductive. Deductive logic includes the logic of Aristotle and also modern symbolic logic. Symbolic logic can be divided into sentential logic and predicate logic.

Aristotelian logic is limited because it can deal only with four types of sentences, sentences we call "categorical sentences". Symbolic logic is far more comprehensive than the older logic because it can deal with many more sentences than just the four categorical sentences. Just as quantum mechanics does not negate the older classical mechanics, symbolic logic does not negate traditional Aristotelian logic. Classical mechanics is a special case of quantum mechanics; Aristotelian logic is a special case of symbolic logic. In other words, symbolic logic can do everything that Aristotelian logic can do plus a lot more besides.

Chapter 1
Traditional Logic

Truth vs. Validity

What is logic?

LOGIC is the science of correct reasoning. In other words, logic is the study of the nature of sound thinking.

Logic deals with premises, conclusions, and arguments.

A PREMISE is an assumption that is used as a basis for inferring a conclusion. A premise is the foundation of your argument.

A CONCLUSION is the statement inferred from the premises.

An ARGUMENT is a formulation that derives a conclusion from the premises. Contrary to popular belief, an argument is not something you have with your spouse. That is a "disagreement"!

If your great-great-grandfather took a course in logic, he was introduced to the following syllogism, the most famous syllogism of them all:

> All men are mortal.
> Socrates is a man.
> Therefore, Socrates is mortal.

What is the premise of this syllogism? What is the conclusion? What is the argument?

See the end of this section for the answers to these questions. Try to answer the questions yourself before you look at the answers.

What is truth? Various philosophers have tried to answer this question. Perhaps the three most famous theories of truth are the following.

The CORRESPONDENCE THEORY of truth holds that a statement is true when it is consistent with facts as they really are. In other words, the correspondence theory asserts that truth is an approximation of thought to reality. If my idea "corresponds" to the facts of the world as they really are, then my idea is true.

The COHERENCE THEORY of truth holds that a statement is true if it is consistent with a coherent body of existing knowledge. In other words, a statement is true if it is logically consistent with other statements accepted as true.

The <u>PRAGMATIC THEORY</u> of truth holds that ideas that are successful in resolving problems are true; ideas that do not lead to satisfactory resolutions are false. In other words, an idea is true if it works successfully to solve the problem it was intended to solve.

So, What is truth? Well, pick the theory you think best.

I regret to have to tell you that logic does not deal with the truth. Logic deals with validity. <u>VALIDITY</u> is a property of an argument whose conclusion logically follows from its premises.

We have valid arguments with true conclusions and valid arguments with false conclusions. Here is an example of a valid argument with a true conclusion:

> All men are mortal.
> Socrates is a man.
> Therefore, Socrates is mortal.

Here is an example of a valid argument with a false conclusion:

> All creatures that fly have wings.
> All pigs fly.
> Therefore, all pigs have wings.

This is a perfect argument. The conclusion follows logically from the premises. Yet its conclusion is false. What went wrong? The argument was polluted by a false premise. If you pollute your argument with a false premise, of course, the conclusion will be false!

An invalid argument is one in which the conclusion does not follow from the premises. <u>INVALIDITY</u> means that the conclusion goes beyond the information provided by the premises. We have invalid arguments with true conclusions and invalid arguments with false conclusions. Here is an invalid argument with a true conclusion:

> If I owned all the gold in Fort Knox, then I would be wealthy.
>
> I do not own all the gold in Fort Knox.
>
> Therefore, I am not wealthy.

This conclusion does not follow from those premises. Nevertheless, for you and me, the conclusion is true. (If your name were Vanderbilt, Rockefeller, or Astor, then the conclusion would be false.)

Here is an invalid argument with a false conclusion:

All terrorists are subversive.
All terrorists are critics of the Administration.
Therefore, all critics of the Administration are subversive.

There is a big difference between truth and validity. Logic deals primarily with validity rather than truth. Logic can guarantee only one thing: If the premises of an argument are all true and there have been no mistakes in reasoning, then logic can guarantee that the conclusion is true.

Suggested Websites:
http://www.earlham.edu/~peters/courses/log/tru-val.htm
http://philosophy.hku.hk/think/arg/valid1.php
http://philosophy.lander.edu/logic/tvs.html
www.philosophypages.com/lg/e01.htm

Answers:
The premises are the first two sentences.
The conclusion is the third sentence (the sentence following the word "therefore").
The argument is all three sentences or the entire syllogism.

Categorical Propositions

Aristotle invented logic in ancient Athens about 350 B.C. Aristotle's logic deals with categorical sentences. There are only four categorical sentences: the "A" sentence, the "E" sentence, the "I" sentence, and the "O" sentence.

The "A" SENTENCE is any sentence of the form "All S are P", where "S" stands for the "subject term" and "P" stands for the "predicate term". An example would be "All Southerners are Protestant" or "All cats are mammals".

The "E" SENTENCE is any sentence of the form "No S are P". For example, "No Southerners are Protestant" or "No Republicans are liberal".

The "I" SENTENCE is any sentence of the form "Some S are P". For example, "Some Southerners are Protestant" or "Some philosophers are idealists".

The "O" SENTENCE is any sentence of the form "Some S are not P". For example, "Some Southerners are not Protestant" or "Some automobiles are not reliable".

Every categorical sentence has something called "quantity" and "quality". The quantity of a categorical sentence can be either universal or particular. It is universal when it says something about every member of the subject term, for example, "All S are P" or "No S are P". It is particular when it refers to only some of the members of the subject term, for example, "Some S are P" or "Some S are not P".

5

The quality of a categorical proposition can be either affirmative or negative. It is affirmative when it asserts that the predicate belongs to the subject, for example, "All S are P" or "Some S are P". It is negative when it asserts that the predicate does not belong to the subject, for example, "No S are P" or "Some S are not P".

Consequently, the "A" sentence is *universal affirmative*. The "E" sentence is *universal negative*. The "I" sentence is *particular affirmative*. And the "O" sentence is *particular negative*.

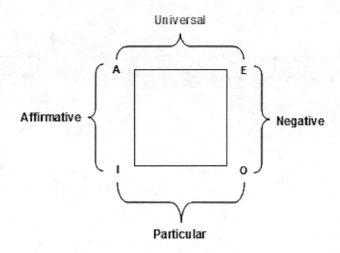

Every categorical sentence is composed of four parts: a quantifier, a subject term, a copula, and a predicate term. The quantifier can be either universal or particular. That is, it can refer to every member of the subject term or merely some members of the subject term. The copula is what couples the subject term with the predicate term. The copula can be either affirmative or negative. That is, it can either assert that the predicate belongs to the subject or deny that the predicate belongs to the subject.

One thing is very important for you to remember! We use the word "some" in logic differently than the way we use it in ordinary conversation. In ordinary conversation, "some" means "a few but not all". In logic "some" means "at least one and perhaps all". If you keep this in mind, you will avoid a lot of trouble for yourself later on.

Now let's try to present each of the four categorical sentences in the form of a diagram. Consider the sentence "All Swedes are Protestant". I will draw one circle to represent all Swedes and an overlapping circle to represent all Protestants.

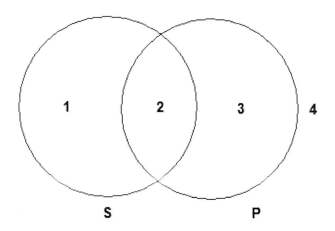

The overlapping circles result in four distinct sets. Set 1 contains all those Swedes who are not Protestant.

What does set 2 (the football-shaped area) contain?
What does set 3 (the crescent-shaped area) contain?
What does set 4 contain?

See the end of this section for the answers to these questions. Try to answer the questions yourself before looking at the answers.

Let's diagram the "A" sentence, "All Swedes are Protestant". Where are Swedes that <u>are</u> Protestant? Set 2. Where are the Swedes that <u>are not</u> Protestant? Set 1. We hatch out Set 1 to indicate that the set is empty because our sentence says, "All Swedes are Protestant".

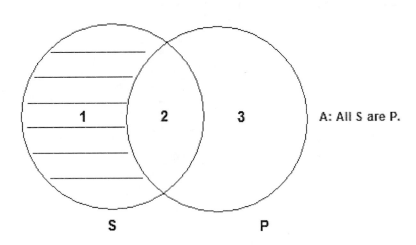

Let's diagram the "E" sentence, "No Swedes are Protestant". Where are the Swedes that are not Protestant? Set 1. Where are the Swedes that are Protestant? Set 2. We hatch out Set 2 to indicate that the set is empty because our sentence says, "No Swedes are Protestant".

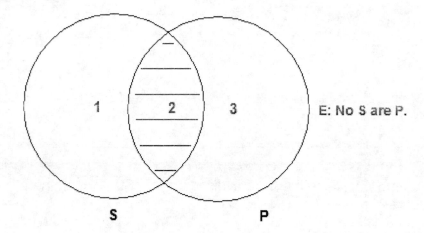

Let's diagram the "I" sentence, "Some Swedes are Protestant". Where are the Swedes that are not Protestant? Set 1. Where are the Swedes that are Protestant? Set 2. We put an asterisk in Set 2 to indicate that there is at least one Swede who is Protestant.

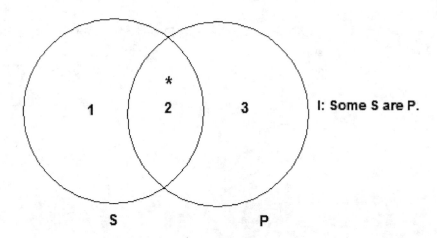

Let's diagram the "O" sentence, "Some Swedes are not Protestant". Where are the Swedes that are Protestant? Set 2. Where are the Swedes that are not Protestant? Set 1. We put an asterisk in Set 1 to indicate that there is at least one Swede who is not a Protestant.

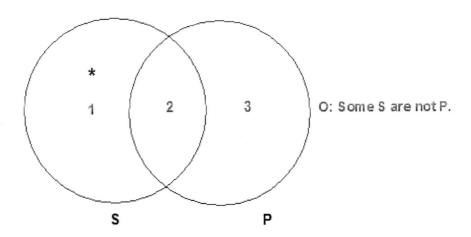

O: Some S are not P.

Something else to remember: <u>All universal sentences are diagramed by hatching something out</u>. If you are diagramming an "E" sentence, you hatch out the football-shaped area. If you are diagramming an "A" sentence, you hatch out either the right or left crescent-shaped area. <u>All particular sentences are diagramed by an asterisk</u>.

Why do I see students diagramming "A" sentences like "E" sentences and "E" sentences like "A" sentences? Because they forget what their teacher told them to remember!

Answers:
Set 2 contains Swedes who are Protestant.
Set 3 contains Protestants who are not Swedes.
Set 4 contains all those who are neither Swedes nor Protestant. This set will include all your Italian Hindus and your Irish Buddhists.

Venn Diagrams

Is the following argument valid or invalid?

All Pakistanis are Muslims.
No Singhalese are Muslims.
Therefore, no Singhalese are Pakistanis.

To simplify things, let's rewrite this argument the short way:

All P are M.
No S are M.
Therefore, no S are P.

We can determine validity by means of a Venn diagram. Since there are three terms in this argument (Pakistanis, Singhalese, and Muslims), we will need one circle for each term. Three overlapping circles will give us eight sets altogether.

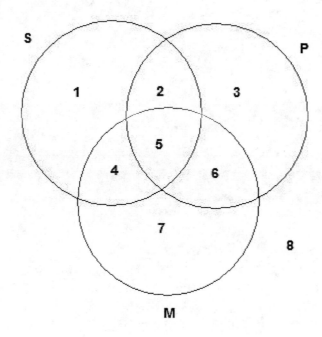

Set one (1) is composed of Singhalese who are neither Pakistanis nor Muslims. Set two (2) is composed of all those people who are Singhalese and Pakistanis but not Muslim.

> Who is in set three (3)?
> Who is in set four (4)?
> Who is in set five (5)?
> Who is in set six (6)?
> Who is in set seven (7)?
> Who is in set eight (8)?

The answers to these questions are at the end of this section. Answer the questions before looking at the answers.

Let's do a Venn diagram on this syllogism to see if it is valid or invalid. We diagram the premises (and <u>only</u> the premises) and then we inspect to see if the conclusion follows from the premises.

Let's diagram the first premise. Since "All P are M", we will eliminate any "P" that are outside of "M". So we hatch out the crescent-shaped area of sets 2 and 3 to indicate they are empty. In this case, ignore the "S" circle.

Let's diagram the second premise. Since "No S are M", we will eliminate any "S" that are "M". So we hatch out the football-shaped area of sets 4 and 5 to indicate they are empty. In this case, ignore the "P" circle.

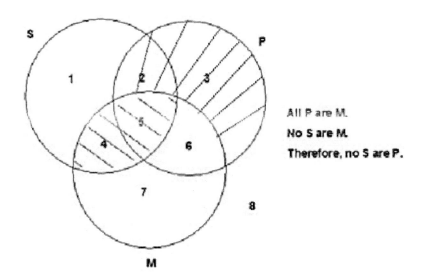

All P are M.
No S are M.
Therefore, no S are P.

That is all we do: we diagram the premises and then inspect to see if the conclusion follows. The conclusion says, "No S are P". If there were an "S" that was also a "P", where would it be? In sets 2 or 5. The diagram says that sets 2 and 5 are empty. Therefore there are no "S" that are also "P". So this syllogism is valid.

Let's try another example. Is the following syllogism valid or invalid?

Some vicious dogs are unsafe animals.
No unsafe animals are good companions for children.
Therefore, no vicious dogs are good companions for children.

Let's rewrite the argument the short way:

Some V are U.
No U are G.
Therefore, No V are G.

Let's diagram the first premise, "Some V are U". Where are the "V" that are also in "U"? In sets 2 and 5. The premise tells us that there is at least one "V" that is also "U", but we cannot be sure where it is. It could be in set 2 while set 5 is empty. Or it could be in set 5 while set 2 is empty. Or it could be that some are in set 2 <u>and</u> some in set 5. We do not know which of these three possibilities is the case. All we know for sure is that there is at least one "V" that is also "U" somewhere in the football-shaped area composed of sets 2 and 5. So we put a "bar" between sets 2 and 5 to indicate that somewhere in that football-shaped area there is at least one "V" that is also "U".

Let's diagram the second premise, "No U are G". Where are the "U" that are "G"? In sets 5 and 6. So we hatch out sets 5 and 6 to indicate that these sets are empty.

Now let's return to the first premise, "Some V are U". Since the second premise has told us that set 5 is empty, we now know that the "V" that is also "U" must to be in set 2. So we put an asterisk in set 2 to indicate that.

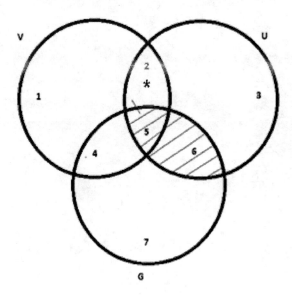

That is all we do: we diagram the premises and then inspect to see if the conclusion follows. The conclusion says, "No V are G". Where are the "V" that are also "G"? In sets 4 and 5. But we do not know anything about set 4. The premises have given us information about only three sets: 2, 5, and 6. By making an assertion about set 4, the conclusion has gone beyond the information of the premises. A syllogism is invalid when its conclusion goes beyond the information provided by its premises. So this syllogism is invalid.

Ask yourself this question: What would the diagram have to look like if this syllogism were to be valid?

The answer to this question is at the end of this section. Think about it first, and then look at the answer.

Let's try one more example. Is the following syllogism valid or invalid?

No logicians are creative.
Some philosophers are not creative.
Therefore, some philosophers are logicians.

Let's rewrite the argument the short way:

> No L are C.
> Some P are not C.
> Therefore, some P are L.

Let's diagram the first premise, "No L are C". Where are the "L" who are also "C"? We hatch out sets 2 and 5 to indicate they are empty. Now the second premise, "Some P are not C". Where are the "P" that are not "C"? We put a bar between sets 4 and 7 to indicate that in this crescent-shaped area there is at least one "P" that is outside of "C".

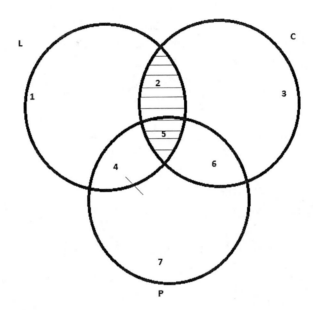

That is all we do: we diagram the premises and then inspect to see if the conclusion follows. The conclusion is "Some P are L". Is the syllogism valid or invalid? It is invalid because all we know for sure is that there is at least one "P" who is outside of "C". It could be in set 4 but not in set 7, or it could be in 7 but not in 4, or it could be in both sets 4 and 7. We cannot be sure which of the three possibilities is the case.

Ask yourself: What would the diagram look like if this syllogism were valid?

Find the answer at the end of this section.

Test yourself on the following syllogism. Is it valid or invalid?

> All police searches without a warrant are violations of civil liberties.
> Some police searches without a warrant are socially justifiable actions.
> Therefore, some socially justifiable actions are violations of civil liberties.

Use the symbols P, V, S to write the syllogism the short way. Then, construct a Venn diagram to determine validity.

See the end of this section for the solution.

Suggested Websites:

http://philosophy.hku.hk/think/misc/sitemap.php
(click on "Module V: Venn Diagrams")
http://philosophy.lander.edu/logic/venn_prop.html
www.philosophypages.com/lg/e08a.htm

Answers:

Set 3 contains Pakistanis who are neither Singhalese nor Muslim.
Set 4 contains Singhalese who are Muslim but not Pakistani.
Set 5 contains all those who are Singhalese, Pakistani, and Muslim.
Set 6 contains those who are Pakistani and Muslim but not Singhalese.
Set 7 contains Muslims who are neither Singhalese nor Pakistani.
Set 8 contains all those who are neither Singhalese, Pakistani, nor Muslim.

The syllogism about the vicious dogs would be valid if and only if sets 4 and 5 were hatched out, indicating that they are empty.

The syllogism about logicians and philosophers would be valid if there were an asterisk in set 4.

Here is the solution for the "house searching without a warrant" syllogism.

All P are V.
Some P are S.
Therefore, some S are V.

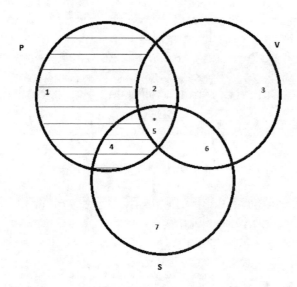

The syllogism is valid. But is the conclusion true? I ask you this question as a good American, an American who believes in the Constitution and the Bill of Rights. Despite what the courts may or may not have decided, searches without a warrant go against both the spirit and the letter of the Bill of Rights. Consequently, all good Americans would say that this conclusion is false. So here is yet another example of the difference between validity and truth!

Remember that premises and conclusions are either true or false; arguments are either valid or invalid.

Exercise 1

DIRECTIONS: Use a Venn diagram to determine the validity of the following arguments.

1. All Republicans are patriotic. All conservatives are Republicans. Therefore, all conservatives are patriotic.

2. No delegates are laughable. Some senators are laughable. So some senators are not delegates.

3. All ex-husbands are idealists. Some employers are not ex-husbands. So some employers are not idealists.

4. No Americans are idealists. All Englishmen are idealists. So no Englishmen are Americans.

5. No strawberries are raspberries. No blueberries are raspberries. So no blueberries are strawberries.

6. No pragmatists are idealists. Some empiricists are pragmatists. So some empiricists are not idealists.

7. No Canadians are communists. Some Venezuelans are not communist. So some Venezuelans are not Canadians.

8. All Airedales are vicious. No Chihuahuas are Airedales. So no Chihuahuas are vicious.

9. Some Communist countries are dictatorships. Some liberal countries are not Communist. So some liberal countries are not dictatorships.

10. Some idealists are Americans. All Americans are unrealistic. So some unrealistic persons are idealists.

11. All Bichon Frizes are friendly. No Bichon Frizes are Norwich terriers. So no Norwich terriers are friendly.

12. All pragmatists are agile. Some pragmatists are smart. So some smart people are agile.

13. All Americans are pragmatists. Some pragmatists are not idealists. So some idealists are not Americans.

14. All statisticians are conservative. Some philosophers are not conservative. So some philosophers are not statisticians.

15. No Hondas are limousines. All Hondas are fuel-efficient vehicles. So no fuel-efficient vehicles are limousines.

Existential vs. Hypothetical Viewpoint

Consider the following argument:

All athletes are daredevils.
All racecar drivers are athletes.
Therefore, some racecar drivers are daredevils.

Let's write the argument the short way:

All A are D.
All R are A.
Therefore, some R are D.

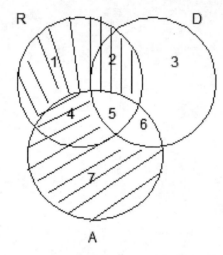

Let me ask you two questions before you decide whether this argument valid or invalid.

First, let me ask you if racecar drivers exist?

Second, if they do exist, what set (from 1-7 of the above diagram) must they be in?

Well, to answer the second question: since sets 1, 2, and 4 are empty sets, they could only be in set 5.

If you believe that racecar drivers exist, then they must be in set 5. You can indicate that with an asterisk.

So is the argument valid or invalid?

If you assume the existential viewpoint, that is, if you assume that racecar drivers exist, then this argument is valid because there is somebody in set 5.

Now let's consider another argument but this time from the <u>hypothetical viewpoint</u>:

> All little people are merry.
> All leprechauns are little people.
> Therefore, some leprechauns are merry.

Let's write the argument the short way:

> All LP are M.
> All L are LP.
> Therefore, some L are M.

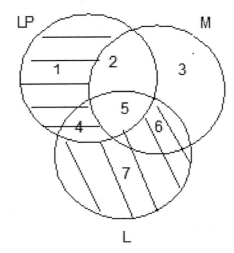

Before you decide if the argument is valid or invalid, let me ask you this question: Do leprechauns exist?

Well who knows? Maybe on Saint Paddy's Day after a couple of beers!

So if you assume the hypothetical viewpoint, that is, if you cannot be sure that leprechauns exist, then you cannot be sure there is somebody in set 5. So you cannot put an asterisk in set 5. Since there is no asterisk in set 5, this argument is invalid.

Let's consider one more example:

> All leprechauns are little green people.
> All little green people are Irish.
> Therefore, all leprechauns are Irish.

Let's write the argument the short way:

> All L are LGP.
> All LGP are I.
> Therefore, all L are I.

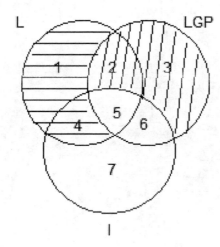

Is this argument valid or invalid? This argument is valid. The conclusion is an "A" sentence. An "A" sentence does not assert existence. Only the "I" and "O" sentences assert existence because "some", in logic, means *at least one* of these things exists. So you do not need an asterisk in set 5 for it to be valid, as you would if the conclusion were a particular sentence. The "A" sentence does not assert existence. Since sets 1, 2, and 4 are empty, "L" has to be in set 5, which is also "I". Of course, all leprechauns are Irish! Who ever heard of an Italian leprechaun?

Mood and Figure

A <u>CATEGORICAL SYLLOGISM</u> is an argument consisting of three categorical sentences, containing three terms in all, each term appearing in two different sentences. Here is the most famous of all categorical syllogisms:

> All men are mortal.
> Socrates is a man.
> Therefore, Socrates is mortal.

The <u>MAJOR TERM</u> is the predicate of the conclusion.
The <u>MINOR TERM</u> is the subject of the conclusion.
The <u>MIDDLE TERM</u> is the term appearing in each of the premises but not in the conclusion.
The <u>MAJOR PREMISE</u> is the premise containing the major term.
The <u>MINOR PREMISE</u> is the premise containing the minor term.

What is the major term of the most famous of all categorical syllogisms?

What is the minor term?

What is the middle term?

Which is the major premise?
Which is the minor premise?

See the end of this section for the answers to these questions.

Next, we will consider <u>mood</u> and <u>figure</u>. To get the mood and figure correct, you must first put the categorical syllogism in the appropriate order. <u>The appropriate order for a categorical syllogism is</u>: the major premise comes first, the minor premise comes second, and the conclusion comes third. Remember that if you do not put the syllogism in the appropriate order, you will get the mood and figure wrong!

The <u>MOOD is the categorical forms of the sentences in the appropriate order</u>. Consider the following syllogism.

> All P are M.
> No S are M.
> Therefore, no S are P.

The major premise is an "A" sentence, the minor premise is an "E" sentence, and the conclusion is an "E" sentence. So the mood is AEE.

What is the mood of the following syllogism?

> All men are mortal.
> Socrates is a man.
> Therefore, Socrates is mortal.

Although it may appear that the statement "Socrates is a man" is an "I" sentence, it is actually an "A" sentence. The statement says, "All people identical to Socrates are men". It does <u>not</u> say, "Some people identical to Socrates are men". Any sentence that begins with a particular person, place, or thing can easily be converted into an "A" sentence. Put the following sentence into categorical form: "San Francisco is in California".

See the end of this section for the answer. Write down your answer to this question and the next two questions before you look at the end of this section.

What is the mood of the most famous syllogism of all? See the end of this section for the answer.

What is the mood of the following syllogism?

> All M are S.
> Some P are M.
> Therefore, some S are P.

See the end of this section for the answer.

The <u>FIGURE refers to the arrangement of the middle terms of a syllogism that is in the appropriate order</u>. In the following diagram, "S" stands for *minor term,* "P" stands for *major term,* and "M" stands for *middle term.* There are four figures: 1, 2, 3, and 4.

1		2		3		4	
M	P	P	M	M	P	P	M
S	M	S	M	M	S	M	S

In figure 1, the middle term appears in the subject place of the major premise and the predicate place of the minor premise. In figure 2, the middle term appears in the predicate place of both premises. In figure 3, the middle term appears in the subject place of both premises. And in figure 4, the middle term appears in the predicate place of the major premise and the subject place of the minor premise.

You have already determined the mood of the three syllogisms above. Now determine the figure for each of them.

See the end of this section for the answers. No cheating!

How many different syllogisms are possible? For the major premise, there are four possibilities. The major premise could be an A, E, I, or O sentence. There are also four possibilities for the minor premise (A, E, I, or O). And there are four possibilities for the conclusion (A, E, I, or O). In addition, a syllogism has one of four figures (1, 2, 3, or 4). So 4 x 4 x 4 x 4 = 256 possible syllogisms, but only 15 of them are valid. How can we determine which are valid?

See the end of this section for the answer.

Please do not forget the difference between the hypothetical viewpoint and the existential viewpoint. In the hypothetical viewpoint, you do not take existence into consideration. But in the existential viewpoint, you are absolutely certain that the thing under discussion exists. From the hypothetical viewpoint, only 15 combinations of mood and figure are valid:

Figure 1	Figure 2	Figure 3	Figure 4
AAA	EAE	IAI	AEE
EAE	AEE	AII	IAI
AII	EIO	OAO	EIO
EIO	AOO	EIO	

From the existential viewpoint, 9 additional combinations are valid:

Figure 1	Figure 2	Figure 3	Figure 4	Required Assumption
AAI EAO	AEO EAO		AEO	Minor term exists
		AII EAO	EAO	Middle term exists
			AAI	Major term exists

Answers:

The major term is "mortal".
The minor term is "Socrates".
The middle term is "men".
The major premise is "All men are mortal".
The minor premise is "Socrates is a man".

Put into categorical form, our sentence says, "All places identical to San Francisco are places that are in California".

The mood of the most famous syllogism is AAA.

The mood of the next syllogism is IAI. (If you do not put the syllogism in the appropriate order, you will get the mood wrong! The appropriate order is: the major premise comes first, the minor premise comes second, and the conclusion comes third.)

The figure of the first syllogism is 2.
The figure of the most famous syllogism is 1.
The figure of the third syllogism is 4. (If you do not put the syllogism in the appropriate order, you will get the figure wrong!)

We can determine the validity of any syllogism by means of a Venn diagram.

Exercise 2

<u>DIRECTIONS</u>: Use a Venn diagram to determine the validity of the following arguments. Then specify the mood and figure of each argument.

1. No Mormons are agnostic. Some empiricists are agnostic. So some empiricists are not Mormons.

2. Some symphonies are not programmatic. No symphonies are concertos. So some concertos are programmatic.

3. No idealists are empiricists. Some existentialists are idealists. So some existentialists are empiricists.

4. No empiricists are idealists. All positivists are empiricists. So no positivists are idealists.

5. All empiricists are materialists. All positivists are materialists. So all positivists are empiricists.

6. All novels are fiction. Some short stories are fiction. So some short stories are novels.

7. All Democrats are liberal. Some radicals are Democrats. So some radicals are liberal.

8. All things composed of atoms are composed of energy, since all things composed of energy are composed of matter, and all things composed of matter are composed of atoms.

9. All symphonies are melodic. Hence, all symphonies are lyrical, for some melodies are lyrical.

10. Some legalists are not barristers because some barristers are not conservative, and all legalists are conservative.

The Rules of the Syllogism

Another way to determine validity is by the *rules of the syllogism*. In order to understand the rules of the syllogism, we first must understand <u>distribution of terms</u>. The subject term of a categorical sentence is distributed if and only if the sentence says something about every member of the set. Consider the "A" sentence, "All cats are good companions". The subject term is distributed because it refers to <u>every</u> member of the set of cats. Consider the "E" sentence, "No cats are good companions". The subject term is distributed because it excludes <u>every</u> member of the set of cats. Consider the "I" sentence, "Some cats are good companions". The subject term is undistributed because it refers to only <u>some</u> members of the set of cats. Consider the "O" sentence, "Some cats are not good companions". The subject term is undistributed because it refers to only <u>some</u> members of the set of cats.

The predicate term of a categorical sentence is distributed if and only if the sentence says something about every member of the set. Consider the "A" sentence, "All cats are good companions". The predicate term is undistributed because cats may be good companions to relax with but they are not good companions to have an intellectual discussion with. Consider the "E" sentence, "No cats are good companions". The predicate term is distributed because cats are excluded from the whole set of good companions. Consider the "I" sentence, "Some cats are good companions". The predicate term is undistributed because it does not refer to every kind of good companion, but only those kinds of good companions that some cats are (good to relax with but not good to have an intellectual discussion with). Consider the "O" sentence, "Some cats are not good companions". The predicate term is distributed because the cats referred to are excluded from the whole set of good companions.

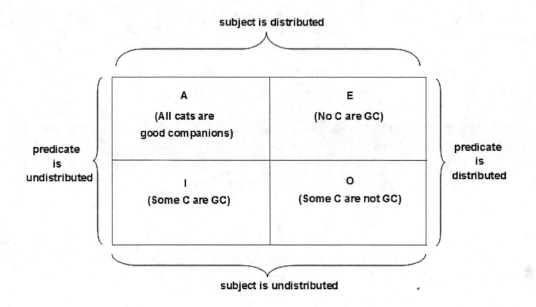

Now we are ready for the rules of the syllogism. If the syllogism disobeys any one of these five rules, then the syllogism is invalid:

1. The middle term must be distributed in at least one premise.
   If a syllogism disobeys this rule, it commits the fallacy of *undistributed middle.*

2. Any term that is distributed in the conclusion must be distributed in the premise.
   If a syllogism disobeys this rule, it commits the fallacy of *illicit major* or *illicit minor.*

3. You cannot have two negative premises.
   If a syllogism disobeys this rule, it commits the fallacy of *exclusive premises.*

4. If either premise is negative, the conclusion must be negative.
   If a syllogism disobeys this rule, it commits the fallacy of *drawing an affirmative conclusion from a negative premise.*
   If the conclusion is negative, at least one premise must be negative. If a syllogism disobeys this rule, it commits the fallacy of *drawing a negative conclusion from affirmative premises.*

5. From the hypothetical viewpoint, a particular conclusion cannot have two universal premises.
   If a syllogism disobeys this rule, it commits the *existential fallacy.*

Suggested Websites:

http://philosophy.lander.edu/logic/syllogism_topics.html
(click under "Syllogistic Fallacies")
www.philosophypages.com/lg/e08b.htm

Exercise 3

Test the following syllogisms for validity using the five rules of the syllogism. If the syllogism is invalid, name the fallacy.

1. Some philosophers are not idealists.
    All philosophers are rational.
    Therefore, some rational people are not idealists.

2. No realists are abstractionists.
    No abstractionists are surrealists.
    Therefore, no surrealists are realists.

3. All emotivists are subjectivists.
    No idealists are emotivists.
    Therefore, all idealists are subjectivists.

4. All opera singers are actors.
    Some singers are opera singers.
    Therefore, some singers are actors.

5. Some politicians are honest.
    All honest persons are reliable.
    Therefore, some reliable people are politicians.

6. Some historians are propagandists.
    Some philosophers are historians.
    Therefore, some philosophers are propagandists.

7. Some musicians are not modernists.
    Some musicians are not classicists
    Therefore, some classicists are not modernists.

8. Some Logical Positivists are not idealists.
    No idealists are empiricists.
    Therefore, all empiricists are Logical Positivists.

9. No poets are novelists.
    Some composers are poets.
    Therefore, some composers are not novelists.

10. All logicians are rational.
    No romantic poets are rational.
    Therefore, no romantic poets are logicians.

Exercise 4

Test the following syllogisms for validity using the five rules of the syllogism. If the syllogism is invalid, name the fallacy.

1. Some musicians are modernists.
   Some modernists are atonalists.
   Therefore, some atonalists are musicians.

2. Some musicians are inspired.
   Some artists are not inspired.
   So some artists are not musicians.

3. Some dramas are not tragedies.
   Some dramas are not comedies.
   So no comedies are tragedies.

4. All musicians are melodists.
   No musicians are atonalists.
   So no atonalists are melodists.

5. No works of genius are superficial.
   Some works of genius are subtle.
   So some subtle works are not superficial.

6. No ideas of Aristotle are ideas expressed in the *Republic*.
   All ideas expressed in the *Republic* are ideas of Plato.
   So some ideas of Plato are not ideas of Aristotle.

7. Some speculative philosophy is not realistic.
   Some of Hegel's ideas are realistic.
   So some of Hegel's ideas are speculative.

8. All musicians are romantic.
   Some romantic people are inspired.
   So some inspired people are musicians.

9. All philosophers are rational.
   No romantic poets are rational.
   So no romantic poets are philosophers.

10. All philosophers are rationalists.
    No rationalists are romanticists.
    So no romanticists are philosophers.

Exercise 5

Translate each sentence into standard categorical form: A, E, I, or O.

1. Architects claim to have artistic talent.

2. Some disciples of Kant were disciples of Leibniz.

3. Potters are all skilled craftsmen.

4. Pollack is an abstract expressionist.

5. A painting by Rembrandt hangs in the local art museum.

6. A photograph is a likeness recorded by a camera.

7. All photographers are not users of Kodak Brownies.

8. Only geniuses are virtuosi.

9. Only some of Picasso's paintings were done during his cubistic period.

10. When Hemmingway writes he must have silence.

11. Some men smoke.

12. "All's well that ends well."

13. Any contribution is appreciated.

14. Cats are carnivorous.

15. "Children are present."

16. There are black swans.

17. Nothing is both in motion and stationary.

18. Only some students were at the game.

19. A flying squirrel is not a bird.

20. A lion escaped.

21. Only citizens can vote in the election.

22. None but men study engineering.

23. Not all cats are Persian.

Chapter 2
Sentential Logic

In Chapter 2 and Chapter 3, we will investigate <u>symbolic logic</u>. The two greatest philosophical advances of the 20th century are the creation of metaethics and the invention of symbolic logic. If there were no symbolic logic, then there would be no computers because computers operate by the laws of symbolic logic. We will begin our study of symbolic logic with the "sentential connectives", which are imitated in the computer by tiny electrical circuits. These sentential connectives are the basis of all the tasks the computer enables us to perform.

The Sentential Connectives

<u>NEGATION</u> is symbolized "~" and means "it is not the case that". So "~p" means "not p".

Negation is always opposite to the sentence negated as regards truth or falsity. We can put this definition of negation into graphic form. On the left side of the graph, we exhaust all the possibilities of truth and falsity for p. The right side of the graph gives the truth-value for "~p".

p	~p
T	F
F	T

<u>DISJUNCTION</u> is symbolized "v" and means "or". So "p v q" means "p or q".

A disjunction is true whenever at least one part is true. We can put this definition into graphic form too. On the left side of the graph, we exhaust all possible combinations of truth and falsity for the component parts of the disjunctive statement: both could both be true, p could be false and the q could be true, p could be true and the q could be false, or both could be false. The right side of the graph gives the truth-value for "p or q".

p	q	p v q
T	T	T
F	T	T
T	F	T
F	F	F

CONJUNCTION is symbolized "•" and means "and". So "p • q" means "p and q".

A conjunction is true when both of its parts are true. We can say this in graphic form:

p	q	p • q
T	T	T
F	T	F
T	F	F
F	F	F

CONDITIONALS is symbolized "⊃" and means "if...then...". So "p ⊃ q" means "if p then q". Every conditional sentence has an antecedent and a consequent. The antecedent [p] comes <u>before</u> the symbol [⊃]; the consequent [q] comes <u>after</u> the symbol [⊃].

A conditional is false when its antecedent is true and its consequent false; otherwise it is true. We can say this in graphic form:

p	q	p ⊃ q	
T	T	T	[line 1]
F	T	T	[line 2]
T	F	F	[line 3]
F	F	T	[line 4]

EQUIVALENCE is symbolized "≡" and means "if and only if". S o "p ≡ q" means "p if and only if q".

An equivalence is true if its parts are alike as regards truth or falsity. We can say this in graphic form:

p	q	p ≡ q
T	T	T
F	T	F
T	F	F
F	F	T

<u>TRUTH FUNCTIONAL SENTENCES</u> are compound sentences (sentences that have at least two parts like: p and q, p or q, if p then q, p if and only if q) whose truth or falsity is determined solely by the truth or falsity of the component parts of the compound sentence. The negation [~] is not a connective because it does not connect two or more parts. It just negates one part.

The four sentential connectives are pretty easy to understand except conditionals [⊃], which is sometimes puzzling. The following simple examples will help you to understand conditionals.

In the first line of the conditional graph above, both components on the left ["p" and "q"] are true, and the compound sentence on the right ["p ⊃ q"] is true. Here is an example: If Barack Obama wins the 2008 presidential election, he will live in Washington, D.C. The antecedent is true: Barack Obama did win the 2008 presidential election. The consequent is true: he did live in Washington, D.C. And the whole statement is true.

Let's consider the second line of the conditional graph where the antecedent is false and the consequent is true [on the left], and the compound sentence is true [on the right]. This is sort of like being right but for the wrong reasons. Here is an example. Gertrude Stein (the famous American poet, you know, "A rose is a rose is a rose!") was never a mother because she too busy carrying on with Alice B. Toklas (who, by the way, made wonderful brownies laced with marijuana). Anyway, Gertrude Stein, or some other woman who was never a mother, could have said, "If I am a mother, then I am a female". In Gertrude Stein's case, the antecedent is false, the consequent is true, and the whole statement is true.

Let's consider the third line of the conditional graph. This one is like drawing a bad conclusion from a good reason. Say you go to the beach one afternoon during the summer. The warm sun is shining down and you happen to look up at the blue sky and see the moon. It looks like someone drew the moon in the sky with chalk. Someone says, "If the moon is visible, then it is nighttime". In this case, the antecedent is true ["the moon is visible"], the consequent is false ["it is nighttime"], and the whole statement is false.

Finally, let's consider the fourth line of the conditional graph. This line says that something false logically follows from something false. Consider this example: If there are unicorns, then there are leprechauns. The antecedent is false and the consequent is false. But the whole statement is true because something ridiculous follows from something ridiculous. I mean, if a quarter is worth 20¢, then 2 quarters are worth 40¢. Right?

SOMETHING ELSE TO REMEMBER:

Do not get equivalence and conditionals mixed up. The following symbolic sentence tells you what equivalence [p ≡ q] means:

$$(p \equiv q) \equiv [(p \supset q) \bullet (q \supset p)].$$

This compound sentence says: "p if and only if q" means the same thing as "If you have a p, then you have a q; and if you have a q, then you have a p".

Conditionals [p ⊃ q] say something entirely different. Nevertheless, sometimes students think "p ⊃ q" means "If you have a p, then you have a q; and if you have a q, then you have a p". It does not! (p ⊃ q) means "If you have a p, then you have a q; but you can have a q under other conditions than p". For example, "If I kill someone, then I'll go to jail; but I can end up in jail for other reasons than killing, for example, I could be sent to jail for writing a bad check".

The following symbolic sentence tells you what conditionals [p ⊃ q] mean:

$$(p \supset q) \equiv \sim(p \bullet \sim q).$$

This compound sentence says: "If p then q" says the same thing as "It is impossible [~] to have a p and not have a q".

How would you symbolize this sentence?: "P only if q". This sentence says, "The only time you have p is if you have a q, but you may have q and not have a p". So "p only if q" means the same thing as "(p ⊃ q)". WHAT IS THE MORAL OF THE STORY? Do not get "only if" confused with "if and only if".

There are three ways that you can express conditionals: "(p ⊃ q)" or "~(p • ~q)" or "p only if q". Here is a simple example to help keep these three identical statements clear in your mind:

1) An example of "(p ⊃ q)" is "If the light bulb is on, then the electricity is working".

2) An example of "~(p • ~q)" is "It is not the case that the light bulb could be on and the electricity NOT be working".

3) An example of "p only if q" is "The light bulb is on only if the electricity is working". These three statements say exactly the same thing but in different words.

So now you know the difference between "only if" and "if and only if". Another word that you must know how to symbolize is "unless". Here is the rule for sentences that contain the word "unless": Negate either part of the "unless sentence" and make it the antecedent of your conditional. Following this rule, symbolize "p unless q" in two different ways.

See the end of this section for the answer.

Summary of the Sentential Connections

p	q		~p	(p • q)	(p v q)	(p ⊃ q)	(p ≡ q)
T	T		F	T	T	T	T
F	T		T	F	T	T	F
T	F		F	F	T	F	F
F	F		T	F	F	T	T

Answer:

Two ways to symbolize "p unless q" following the rule:

(~p ⊃ q) or (~q ⊃ p).

Exercise 6

A. <u>DIRECTIONS</u>: Assume "L" means "you win the lottery" and "V" means "you take a vacation". Match each English sentence with the correct symbolic formula.

1. If you win the lottery, you take a vacation.

2. You do not win the lottery and you do not take a vacation.

3. You win the lottery or you do not take a vacation.

4. You win the lottery if and only if you take a vacation.

5. You do not win the lottery only if you do not take a vacation.

6. You do not take a vacation, if you do not win the lottery.

7. Either you win the lottery or you do not take a vacation.

8. You neither win the lottery nor take a vacation.

9. It is not the case that you win the lottery and do not take a vacation.

10. Unless you win the lottery, you do not take a vacation.

     • a.   ~L • ~V
     • b.   ~(L • ~V)
     •c.   ~L ⊃ ~V
     •d.   L ≡ V
     • e.   ~L ⊃ ~V
     • f.   L v ~V
       g.   ~L ⊃ ~V
     • h.   L ⊃ V
       i.   ~L ⊃ ~V
     • j.   L v ~V

B. <u>DIRECTIONS</u>: Assume "L" means "you win the lottery", "V" means "you take a vacation", and "H" means "you buy a new home". Match each English sentence with the correct symbolic formula.

1. If you win the lottery, then you take a vacation and buy a new home.

2. If you win the lottery and take a vacation, then you will buy a new home.

3. You win the lottery, only if you take a vacation or buy a new home.

4. You win the lottery or take a vacation, if and only if you buy a new home.

5. If you do not win the lottery, you neither take a vacation nor buy a new home.

6. If you do not win the lottery, then either you do not take a vacation or you do not buy a new home.

7. You win the lottery only if you go on vacation, or buy a new home.

8. You win the lottery, if and only if you both take a vacation and buy a new home.

9. You either take a vacation or buy a new home, if you win the lottery.

10. It is not the case that you will win the lottery, and neither take a vacation nor buy a new home.

a. $L \equiv (V \cdot H)$
b. $(L \lor V) \equiv H$
c. $(L \cdot V) \supset H$
d. $L \supset (V \lor H)$
e. $L \supset (V \lor H)$
f. $(L \supset V) \lor H$
g. $L \supset (V \cdot H)$
h. $\sim L \supset (\sim V \cdot \sim H)$
i. $\sim L \supset (\sim V \lor \sim H)$
j. $\sim[L \cdot (\sim V \cdot \sim H)]$

C. <u>DIRECTIONS</u>: Suppose "R" means "Russia is in South America", "S" means "Spain is in Africa", "E" means "Egypt is in Africa", and "F" means "France is in Europe". What is the truth value of the following sentences?

1. $R \lor E$

2. $R \cdot E$

3. $S \equiv R$

4. $F \supset E$

5. $\sim R \supset F$

6. $\sim(R \supset F)$

7. $S \lor (R \lor E)$

8. $R \supset (S \supset F)$

9. $F \supset \sim(R \lor S)$

10. $\sim[S \lor (R \supset S)]$

D. <u>DIRECTIONS</u>: Suppose "W" means "Washington is the capitol of the USA", "M" means "Moscow is the capitol of Russia", "A" means "Ankara is the capitol of France", and "B" means "Bangkok is the capitol of China". What is the truth value of the following sentences?

1. (W • M) • (A • B)

2. (W v A) • (M v B)

3. (A ⊃ W) ⊃ (B ⊃ M)

4. (B ⊃ M) ⊃ (W ⊃ A)

5. (M ⊃ A) v (B ⊃ A)

6. (W ⊃ B) ≡ (M ⊃ A)

7. [(W ⊃ A) ⊃ M] ⊃ [(W • M) ⊃ B]

8. [(W • A) ⊃ (M ⊃ B)] v A

9. ~[(A ⊃ B) v (W ⊃ M)] ≡ (A ⊃ W)

10. [(B • A) ⊃ (A ⊃ W)] • (B v M)

Truth Tables

One way to determine the validity of an argument in symbolic logic is by means of a truth table. A <u>TRUTH TABLE</u> can determine the validity of a compound sentence by considering all the possible combinations of truth or falsity for the component parts of the compound sentence. Our graphs for the sentential connectives ("and", "or", "if...then", "if and only if") are really truth tables. On the right side of the truth table, we wrote the compound sentence we were considering ("p • q", "p v q", "p ⊃ q", or "p ≡ q"). On the left side of the truth table, we exhausted all possible combinations of truth or falsity for the component parts of the compound sentence.

So on the left side of every truth table, we must exhaust all possible combinations of truth and falsity for the component parts of our compound sentence. To construct a truth table, the first thing you must do is to figure out how many lines it will take to exhaust all possible combinations of truth and falsity for the component parts of the compound sentence. Let's say the sentence you are considering consists of only one letter, "p". How many lines will it take to exhaust all the possibilities of truth and falsity? Only two: true and false.

Now let's say that your compound sentence has two letters, "p" and "q". How many lines do you need to exhaust all the possibilities of truth and falsity? It will take four lines: 1) p and q could both be true, 2) p could be false and q true, 3) p could be true and q false, or 4) p and q could both be false.

So if your sentence consists of only one letter, you will have a truth table of two lines. If your compound sentence has two letters, you will have a truth table of four lines. Here is an easy way to figure out how many lines your truth table will have. If your sentence consists of *one* letter, then use 2^1 to get 2 lines. We use 2^1 because there are two possibilities for each letter: true or false, and we use the first power because we have only one letter. If your compound sentence consists of *two* letters, then use 2^2 to get 4 lines. Two to the second power means there are two possibilities for each letter (true and false) and the second power indicates that we are using two letters. Suppose your compound sentence consists of three letters: p, q, r. How many lines must your truth table have? Suppose your compound sentence consists of four letters. How many lines must your truth table have?

Find the answers to these questions at the end of this section.

After you figure out how many lines your truth table will have, the next problem is to make sure you exhaust all the possible combinations of truth and falsity for the component parts of the compound sentence without any repeats. You can accomplish this by the following rule:

1) alternate the entries in the first column (T, F, T , F),

2) pair the entries in the second column (TT, FF, TT, FF),

3)   alternate by fours in the third column (TTTT, FFFF, TTTT, FFFF),

4)   alternate by eights in the fourth column (TTTTTTTT, FFFFFFFF).

Say you meet Bertrand Russell in the cafeteria one morning. You tell him, "Bertie, old chap, I'm talking a course in logic!" He asks, "Well, what are you studying at the moment?" You say, "Symbolic logic". He says, "Well, then: If r and q, then p if and only if r. Valid or invalid?"

How would you go about answering his question?

Of course! You'd do a truth table on it. The first step is to symbolize his compound sentence: (r • q) ⊃ (p ≡ r). Now, let's see, how many lines will the truth table have? Two to the third power is: let me see, 2 x 2 x 2. Oh, eight! OK, so now we can set up the truth table. On the right side we put the compound sentence. On the left side we exhaust all possible combinations of truth and falsity for the component parts of the compound sentence without any repeats: so I alternate in the first column, pair in the second column, and alternate by fours in the third column.

p	q	r	(r	•	q)	⊃	(p	≡	r)
T	T	T							
F	T	T							
T	F	T							
F	F	T							
T	T	F							
F	T	F							
T	F	F							
F	F	F							

Now under the compound sentence on the right, I copy under the "r" the truth values from the "r" column on the left. Under the "q", I copy the "q" values from the left. And under the "p", I copy the "p" values from the left.

p	q	r	(r	•	q)	⊃	(p	≡	r)
T	T	T	T		T		T		T
F	T	T	T		T		F		T
T	F	T	T		F		T		T
F	F	T	T		F		F		T
T	T	F	F		T		T		F
F	T	F	F		T		F		F
T	F	F	F		F		T		F
F	F	F	F		F		F		F

Do you have your chart for the sentential connectives? Have it right in front of you so you can perform the operations. Use the conjunction chart for the antecedent, (r · q). Put the appropriate truth value that you get from the conjunction chart under the "and" column of the compound sentence. Use the equivalence chart for the consequent, (p ≡ r). Put the truth value that you get from the equivalence chart under the "if and only if" column of the compound sentence.

p	q	r	(r	•	q)	⊃	(p	≡	r)
T	T	T	T	T	T	T	T	T	T
F	T	T	T	T	T	F	F	F	T
T	F	T	T	F	F	T	T	T	T
F	F	T	T	F	F	F	F	F	T
T	T	F	F	F	T	T	T	F	F
F	T	F	F	F	T	T	F	T	F
T	F	F	F	F	F	T	T	F	F
F	F	F	F	F	F	T	F	T	F

So how do we figure out if this compound sentence is valid or invalid? Which column will tell us? Of course, the blank column, the "if...then" column. If every single line turns out to be true, then the argument is valid. If there is one or more lines that are false, then the argument is invalid. Now, what two columns do we use to figure out the truth value of the "if...then" column? Right again, you are really getting on to this! Of course, it is the two middle columns. So get your chart for the conditionals and go to work.

If you meet Bertrand Russell in the cafeteria, and he says, "If r and q, then p if and only if r. Right?" What do you say to him?

(Find the answer to this question at the end of this section. Do the work first before looking. No cheating!)

We can prove the validity of the "Chain Argument" by means of a truth table. The chain argument says "If p then q, if q then r, therefore, if p then r". Let's write the chain argument using our symbols; the black line means "therefore":

$$
\begin{array}{ccc}
p & \supset & q \\
q & \supset & r \\
\hline
p & \supset & r
\end{array}
$$

This is the chain argument written vertically. But to do a truth table on it, we have to write the chain argument horizontally rather than vertically. How would we do that? We would have to distinguish the premises from the conclusion so that anyone could clearly see what the premises are and what the conclusion is. We do that by using brackets around the premises to distinguish them from the conclusion:

$$[(p \supset q) \cdot (q \supset r)] \supset (p \supset r)$$

Then we set up a truth table to prove that it is valid.

p	q	r	$[(p \supset q) \cdot (q \supset r)] \supset (p \supset r)$

If you fill in this truth table, you will find that every line under the third conditional will turn out to be true, thus indicating that the argument is valid. Try it for yourself!

Test yourself on the following argument:

If matter exists, then Berkeley was incorrect.
If the world exists, then matter exists.
Therefore, either the world exists or Berkeley was incorrect.

Directions:

1) Use the symbols M, B, and W.
2) Symbolize the argument vertically.
3) Symbolize the argument horizontally.
4) Construct a truth table to determine validity.
5) Is the argument valid or invalid?

Find the answers at the end of this section.

Symbolize the following argument:

If you study both sculpture and painting, then you would like architecture.
But you do not like architecture.
Therefore, if you study sculpture, you do not study painting (S, P, A).

Use the symbols S, P, and A. To symbolize this argument you will need parenthesis (parenthesis), brackets [brackets], and braces {braces}. Always use the parenthesis first. If you need more, use the brackets second. If you need still more, use the braces third.

If you need more practice in determining validity, do a truth table on this example.

Find the answers at the end of this section.

Consider this problem:

Does ~(p · q) mean the same thing as (~p · ~q)? Do a truth table to find out. The challenge you face in this problem is to figure out what symbol you would use for "means the same thing as". Hint: it is one of our four sentential connectives.

Find the answer at the end of this section.

Answers:

How many lines must a truth table have?

A compound sentence of three letters would be 2^3 = 8 lines. A compound sentence of four letters would be 2^4 = 16 lines.

What would you say to Bertrand Russell? You'd say, "No, wrong! The argument is invalid." It is invalid because (p ≡ r) does not follow from (r · q) in every case.

p	q	r	(r	•	q)	⊃	(p	≡	r)
T	T	T	T	T	T	T	T	T	T
F	T	T	T	T	T	F	F	F	T
T	F	T	T	F	F	T	T	T	T
F	F	T	T	F	F	T	F	F	T
T	T	F	F	F	T	T	T	F	F
F	T	F	F	F	T	T	F	T	F
T	F	F	F	F	F	T	T	F	F
F	F	F	F	F	F	T	F	T	F

The Berkeley example:

1) Use M, B, and W.

2) Symbolize the argument vertically:

M ⊃ B
W ⊃ M
W v B

3) Symbolize the argument horizontally:

$$[(M \supset B) \bullet (W \supset M)] \supset (W \lor B)$$

4) Construct a truth table. Always begin with the most interior parenthesis and work on out. In other words, do the parenthesis first, then do the brackets. Then get the truth value for both premises (which you will find under the "and" column). Use the truth value for both premises (which you will find under the "and" column) as the antecedent. Use the truth value for the entire conclusion (which you will find under "or" column) for the consequent. Then find the truth value for the whole argument under the third "if...then" symbol.

M	B	W	[(M ⊃ B)	•	(W ⊃ M)]	⊃	(W v B)
T	T	T	T	T	T	T	T
F	T	T	T	F	F	T	T
T	F	T	F	F	T	T	T
F	F	T	T	F	F	T	T
T	T	F	T	T	T	T	T
F	T	F	T	T	T	T	T
T	F	F	F	F	T	T	F
F	F	F	T	T	T	(F)	F

5) This argument is invalid.

<u>The sculpture, painting, and architecture example:</u>

$$\{[(S \bullet P) \supset A] \bullet \sim A\} \supset (S \supset \sim P)$$

If you do a truth table, always work from the most interior parenthesis on out. So do the parenthesis first, then the brackets, then the braces. This argument is valid.

<u>Does ~(p · q) mean the same thing as (~p · ~q)?</u>

In order to answer the question you would have to symbolize it and do a truth table on it.

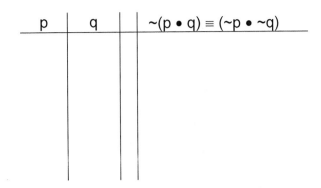

If you do the truth table, you will find that these two propositions *are not* equivalent. Here is "De Morgan's Law": ~(p · q) ≡ (~p v ~q).

If you do a truth table on De Morgan's Law, you will see that it *is* equivalent.

Tautologies & Contradictions

A <u>tautology</u> is a compound sentence which is true whether its component parts are true or false. Give an example of a tautology from the truth tables we have so far considered.

Find the answer at the end of this section. Think about it first before looking.

A <u>contradiction</u> is a compound sentence which is false, whether its component parts are true or false. Here is an example:

p		p	≡	~p
T		T	F	FT
F		F	F	TF

Suppose a truth table turns out to be neither a tautology nor a contradiction. Then, what is it?

Find the answer at the end of this section. Think before looking!

Answers:

<u>An example of a tautology</u> would be De Morgan's Law or any valid argument.

<u>If a truth table is neither a tautology nor a contradiction</u>, then it is either non-equivalent or it is an invalid argument.

Exercise 7

You will find Modus Ponens and the Disjunctive Arguments in the Rules of Inference in Ch 2, Sec 6. Another rule is called the Chain Argument. It is written vertically in the Rules of Inference. In Ch 2, Sec 3, we wrote the Chain Argument horizontally. Please write Modus Ponens and the Disjunctive Arguments horizontally, following the pattern we used with the Chain Argument.

    1.   Modus Ponens
    2.   Disjunctive Arguments

Does a imply b? (In questions 3-6, the challenge is to figure out how to symbolize "implies" and "is implied by". You will have to solve this problem by using our symbols: and, or, if...then, if and only if.)

    3.   a is ~(p v q); b is ~q
    4.   a is (~p ⊃ q); b is (p v q)

Is a implied by b?

    5.   a is ~(p • q); b is ~q
    6.   a is ~(p ⊃ q); b is ~q

Are the following equivalent?

    7.   (p ⊃ ~q) and ~(p ⊃ q)
    8.   (p ≡ ~q) and ~(p ≡ q)

Are the following tautologies, contradictions, or neither? (How do you find out if a statement is a tautology, a contradiction, or neither? Hint: you cannot eye-ball it!)

    9.   p v (q ⊃ q)
    10. (p ≡ ~p) • q

Exercise 8

A. <u>DIRECTIONS</u>: Use a truth table to determine whether the following arguments are valid or invalid. Use symbols "C" and "H". Remember that the symbol (e.g., "C") stands for the whole phrase and not just for one word in the phrase. So "C" stands for "Caesar crossed the Rubicon" and "H" stands for "Hannibal scaled the Alps". If you do not remember that the letter stands for the whole phrase, you are going to get all mixed up.

1. Caesar crossed the Rubicon, and Hannibal scaled the Alps. So Hannibal scaled the Alps.
2. Caesar crossed the Rubicon, and Hannibal scaled the Alps. So Caesar crossed the Rubicon, or Hannibal scaled the Alps.
3. If Hannibal scaled the Alps, Caesar crossed the Rubicon. So if Caesar did not cross the Rubicon, Hannibal did not scale the Alps.
4. If Caesar crossed the Rubicon, Hannibal scaled the Alps. So Caesar crossed the Rubicon if Hannibal scaled the Alps.
5. Hannibal scaled the Alps if and only if Caesar crossed the Rubicon. So Caesar crossed the Rubicon if Hannibal scaled the Alps.
6. Caesar crossed the Rubicon, and Hannibal scaled the Alps. So Hannibal scaled the Alps if and only if Caesar crossed the Rubicon.
7. Hannibal scaled the Alps if and only if Caesar crossed the Rubicon. So Hannibal scaled the Alps and Caesar crossed the Rubicon.
8. It is not the case both that Caesar crossed the Rubicon and Hannibal scaled the Alps. So it is not the case that either Hannibal scaled the Alps or Caesar crossed the Rubicon.
9. Hannibal did not scale the Alps and Caesar did not cross the Rubicon. So if Hannibal scaled the Alps, Caesar crossed the Rubicon.
10. Hannibal scaled the Alps or Caesar did not cross the Rubicon. So it is not the case that Caesar crossed the Rubicon if Hannibal scaled the Alps.

B. <u>DIRECTIONS</u>: Use a truth table to determine whether the first symbolic sentence would imply the second symbolic sentence.

1. p; (p v q)
2. (p • ~p); q
3. p; (q v ~q)
4. p≡p;p

C. <u>DIRECTIONS</u>: Use a truth table to determine whether the following symbolic sentences are equivalent.

1. (p ⊃ q); ~(p • ~q)
2. ~(p • ~q); ~p v q
3. (p ⊃ q); (q ⊃ p)
4. ~(p v q); (~p v ~q)

D. <u>DIRECTIONS</u>: Use a truth table to determine which of the following symbolic sentences are tautologies, which are contradictions, and which are neither.

1. A v A
2. (B ≡~B) • A
3. D ⊃ (D v D)
4. D ⊃ ~D
5. H v ~H
6. ~(H • ~H)
7. N v M
8. N v (M ⊃ M)
9. X ≡ W
10. (X • ~X) v W

Exercise 9

Use a truth table to find the solutions to the following problems.

1. Is the following argument valid?

   If Romeo is in love, Juliet has returned his favors. Either Juliet has not returned his favors or Romeo is not in love. Therefore Romeo is in love. (R, J)

2. Are the following sentences logically equivalent?

   If Keats and Shelley were English poets, then Elizabeth Barrett was in love with Robert Browning. If Keats was an English poet, then if Shelley was an English poet then Elizabeth Barrett was in love with Robert Browning. (K, S, E)

3. Is it necessarily true that:

   If Shelley is an English poet, then either Keats did not write *When I Have Fears* or Shelley is an English poet. (S, K)

4. Is the following argument valid?

   If Juliet marries Romeo, then Ophelia is jealous. Ophelia is jealous. Therefore Juliet marries Romeo. (J, O)

5. Does the first sentence imply the second sentence?

   If Shakespeare wrote *Hamlet* then Homer wrote the *Iliad*. If Homer wrote the *Iliad* then Shakespeare wrote *Hamlet*. (S, H)

6. Are the following sentences logically equivalent?

   If Romeo proposes marriage, then Juliet accepts. Either it is not the case that Romeo proposes marriage or Juliet accepts. (R, J)

7. Is the following argument valid or invalid?

   Talleyrand will unseat the French Emperor unless Napoleon discovers the treachery. Czar Alexander will remain discrete but Napoleon discovers the treachery. Therefore either Napoleon discovers the treachery and Talleyrand will not unseat the French Emperor or Napoleon will not discover the treachery and Talleyrand will unseat the French Emperor. (T, N, A)

8. Is this person saying something necessarily false?

   If Shakespeare did not write the *Iliad* then Homer wrote *Hamlet*. (S, H)

Rules of Inference

A symbolic argument of two letters has a truth table of four lines. A symbolic argument of three letters has a truth table of eight lines. A symbolic argument of four letters has a truth table of sixteen lines. This is about as far as we can go with truth tables because a symbolic argument of five letters would have a truth table of thirty-two lines. With thirty-two lines, we would run out of paper!

So we have to find another method of evaluating symbolic arguments. That method is called <u>deduction</u> and it is based on the Rules of Inference. The Rules of Inference are the foundation of symbolic logic, sort of the Bible of symbolic logic. From now on, all our attempts to show the validity of arguments will be based on these Rules of Inference.

There is no need for you to memorize the Rules of Inference. You will use them so often that you will become very familiar with them just from using them. So just go over each rule individually in order to familiarize yourself with it. See if you can understand the reasoning behind it.

RULES OF INFERENCE

 Modus Ponens (MP)   p ⊃ q
$$\frac{p}{q}$$

 Modus Tollens (MT)   p ⊃ q
$$\frac{\sim q}{\sim p}$$

 Chain Argument (CA)   p ⊃ q
$$\frac{q \supset r}{p \supset r}$$

 Disjunctive Arguments (DA)

p ∨ q   p ∨ q
$$\frac{\sim p}{q} \qquad \frac{\sim q}{p}$$

Addition (Add.)

$$\frac{p}{p \lor q} \qquad\qquad \frac{q}{p \lor q}$$

Conjunctive Arguments (Conj. A)

~(p • q)   ~(p • q)
$$\frac{p}{\sim q} \qquad \frac{q}{\sim p}$$

Simplification (Simp.)

$$\frac{p \cdot q}{p} \qquad \frac{p \cdot q}{q}$$

Conjunction (Conj.)   p
$$\frac{q}{p \cdot q}$$

Reductio Ad Absurdum (RAA)

$$\frac{p \supset \sim p}{\sim p} \qquad \frac{p \supset (q \cdot \sim q)}{\sim p}$$

Simple Constructive Dilemma (SCD)

p ⊃ q
r ⊃ q
$$\frac{p \lor r}{q}$$

Simple Destructive Dilemma (SDD)

p ⊃ q
p ⊃ r
$$\frac{\sim q \lor \sim r}{\sim p}$$

Complex Constructive Dilemma (CCD)

p ⊃ q
r ⊃ s
$$\frac{p \lor r}{q \lor s}$$

Complex Destructive Dilemma (CDD)

p ⊃ q
r ⊃ s
$$\frac{\sim q \lor \sim s}{\sim p \lor \sim r}$$

Repetition (REP)

p ≡ (p ∨ p) ≡ (p • p)

 Definition of Material Implication (DMI)

(p ⊃ q) ≡ (~p ∨ q) ≡ ~(p • ~q)

Definition of Material Equivalence (DME)

(p ≡ q) ≡ [(p ⊃ q) • (q ⊃ p)]

Double Negation (DN)

p ≡ ~(~p)

 Contraposition (Contra.)

(p ⊃ q) ≡ (~q ⊃ ~p)

Commutation (Com.)

(p ∨ q) ≡ (q ∨ p)
(p • q) ≡ (q • p)

Association (Assoc.)

[p ∨ (q ∨ r)] ≡ [(p ∨ q) ∨ r]
[p • (q • r)] ≡ [(p • q) • r]

Distribution (Dist.)

[p • (q ∨ r)] ≡ [(p • q) ∨ (p • r)]
[p ∨ (q • r)] ≡ [(p ∨ q) • (p ∨ r)]

 De Morgan's Laws (DeM)

~(p ∨ q) ≡ (~p • ~q)
~(p • q) ≡ (~p ∨ ~q)

Exportation (Exp.)

[(p • q) ⊃ r] ≡ [p ⊃ (q ⊃ r)]

Quantification Equivalences (QE)

(x) Mx ≡ ~(∃x) ~ Mx
(x) ~Mx ≡ ~(∃x) Mx
(∃x) Mx ≡ ~ (x) ~Mx
(∃x) ~Mx ≡ ~(x) Mx

You will use some rules more often than others. I have found that the ones you should consider first when trying to prove the validity of an argument are the following: Modus Ponens, Modus Tollens, Chain Argument, Disjunctive Arguments, Conjunctive Arguments, Definition of Material Implication, Contraposition, and De Morgan's Laws. Print out a copy of the Rules of Inference and mark the ones mentioned above so you will try them first. Students seem to love the four Dilemmas but they are not as useful as the ones I just mentioned.

Look at Modus Ponens. It says: if you have "p ⊃ q" and if you also have "p", then you can derive "q". The premises come first, the black line means "therefore", and the conclusion comes last.

Modus Ponens and Modus Tollens are easy to get mixed up. You will *never* get mixed up if you remember what these Latin words mean. Modus Ponens means "positing the antecedent"; Modus Tollens means "denying the consequent".

The following websites are helpful in describing the Rules of Inference:

www.philosophypages.com/lg/e10b.htm
www.philosophypages.com/lg/e10c.htm
www.philosophypages.com/lg/e11a.htm
www.philosophypages.com/lg/e11b.htm

Deductions

Let's try a first example of deduction:

1)   R v S   Premise
2)   ~R • ~T   Premise
3)   ~R
4)   S

In this example, the first two lines are the premises. Line 4 is the conclusion. Line 3 is the method used to derive the conclusion (line 4) from the premises (lines 1 and 2). What you have to do is to find the previous line and the rule which enables you to derive line 3 and line 4. Then you write that information on the right under "premise".

Let's look at line 3. From what line above it would you be most likely to derive the ~R? Probably from line 2 because that is the only line with a ~R in it. So then you write down line "2":

1)   R v S   Premise
2)   ~R • ~T   Premise
3)   ~R   2,
4)   S

Now find the Rule of Inference that will enable you to derive line 3 from line 2. So look through the Rules of Inference for all the rules with an "and" in the premises. You are hoping to find one that will enable you to isolate one part of the compound "and" statement. Well, the Conjunctive Argument has an "and" in it, Simplification has an "and" in it, Definition of Material Implication has an "and" in it, and De Morgan's Law has an "and" in it. Which one of these four possibilities is most likely to fit the case you are dealing with? You want to isolate one part of the "and" statement. Yes! Simplification allows you to do just that. So now indicate that you derived ~R from line 2 and the rule of Simplification.

1)	R v S	Premise
2)	~R • ~T	Premise
3)	~R	2, Simplification
4)	S	

Now from what line do you think that you can derive the conclusion ("S")? Well, obviously from line 1 since that is the only line that has an "S" in it. Now you have to find a rule that enables you to get one side of a compound "or" statement. So look through the Rules of Inference for all those rules that have an "or" in the premises. Well, the Disjunctive Argument, the Definition of Material Implication, and De Morgans Law all have an "or". Which one would enable you to get one side of a compound "or" statement? Yes! The Disjunctive Argument; but to use the Disjunctive Argument you need two lines because it has two premises. So you have already decided that you will get the "S" from line 1, but what second line do you need to get the "S"? Yes, line 3. Let's test our proposed solution to see if it fits the rule. The rule you are following is the Disjunctive Argument:

$$p \quad v \quad q$$
$$\underline{\sim p}$$
$$q$$

Let's use our lines 1 and 3 and see if you can derive "S":

$$R \quad v \quad S$$
$$\underline{\sim R}$$
$$?$$

Does it work? Yes! So you have solved the problem. All you have remaining to do is to write down which lines and which rule you used to drive the "S":

1)	R v S	Premise
2)	~R • ~T	Premise
3)	~R	2, Simplification
4)	S	1, 3, Disjunctive Argument

<u>Let's try a second example</u> of deduction:

1) ~A v B   Premise
2) ~(B • ~C)   Premise
3) ~B v C
4) B ⊃ C
5) A ⊃ B
6) A ⊃ C

The first two lines are the premises. Line 6 is the conclusion. Line 3 through line 5 is the argument that derives line 6 from the premises. We are asked to say how lines 3-6 were derived by stating from what previous line each was derived and what rule was used to derive it.

From what line above it was line 3 derived? Obviously, line 2. Now look for a rule that can convert an "and" sentence into an "or" sentence. The possibilities are DMI or DeM. Actually each will work; but for the sake of our example, let's pick DeM. DeM says:

$$\sim(p • q) \equiv (\sim p \text{ v} \sim q)$$

Let's follow the rule by using our example (line 2) and see if we can derive line 3:

$$\sim(B • \sim C) \equiv ?$$

Will it work? The negation outside the parenthesis on the left is dropped when we move over to the right side of the equation. The p on the left changes its sign on the right (in this case from positive to negative). The "and" on the left becomes an "or" on the right. And when the q comes over from the left to the right side, its sign is changed (in this case from positive to negative).

OK, so let's try it on our line 3. We drop the negation outside the parentheses. When the B comes over to the right, its sign is changed (in this case from positive to negative). The "and" on the left becomes an "or" on the right. And the ~C on the left changes its sign on the right (in this case from negative to positive). So we get "~B v C". Yes, DeM enables us to get line 3. So we indicate that on our example:

1) ~A v B   Premise
2) ~(B • ~C)   Premise
3) ~B v C   2, DeM
4) B ⊃ C
5) A ⊃ B
6) A ⊃ C

Now on to line 4. From what line above it do you think line 4 was derived? Either from line 2 or line 3. Maybe line 3 would be the better choice because it probably was included for some reason. So let's guess it is from line 3. Now we are looking for a rule that lets us convert from an "or" statement to an "if...then" statement. Which rules enable us to do that? Only one: DMI. Let's see if it enables us to derive line 4 from line 3. DMI says:

$$(\sim p \lor q) \equiv (p \supset q)$$

Let's put in what we have:

$$(\sim B \lor C) \equiv \,?$$

This is an easy one. It works. So we indicate that on our example:

1)	~A v B	Premise
2)	~(B • ~C)	Premise
3)	~B v C	2, DeM
4)	B ⊃ C	3, DMI
5)	A ⊃ B	
6)	A ⊃ C	

Now from what line above it was line 5 derived? It has to be line 1 because that is the only line with an "A" and a "B". Now look for a rule that enables you to convert from an "or" to an "If...then". DMI again. If you are not sure it will work, then write out the rule, put line 1 in, and see it you can derive line 5 from it.

1)	~A v B	Premise
2)	~(B • ~C)	Premise
3)	~B v C	2, DeM
4)	B ⊃ C	3, DMI
5)	A ⊃ B	1, DMI
6)	A ⊃ C	

Finally, from what line did we get line 6. This is going to take two lines: line 5 and line 4. Which rule? CA, which says:

$$\frac{\begin{array}{c} p \supset q \\ q \supset r \end{array}}{p \supset r}$$

Let's put in lines 5 and 4 and see if we can derive line 6:

$$A \supset B$$
$$\underline{B \supset C}$$
$$?$$

Does it work? Yes. So we write in the solution for our example:

1)	~A v B	Premise
2)	~(B • ~C)	Premise
3)	~B v C	2, DeM (or 2, DMI)
4)	B ⊃ C	3, DMI (or 2, DMI)
5)	A ⊃ B	1, DMI
6)	A ⊃ C	5, 4, CA

Let's try a third example of deduction:

1)	~(~E ⊃ F) ⊃ ~(B ⊃ D)	Premise
2)	F v D	Premise
3)	B ⊃ ~F	Premise
4)	(B ⊃ D) ⊃ (~E ⊃ F)	
5)	~F ⊃ D	
6)	B ⊃ D	
7)	~E ⊃ F	
8)	E v F	

From what line above it do you think line 4 was derived.

Line 1 is the obvious choice. Now you are looking for a rule that negates the consequent and converts it into the antecedent and then negates the antecedent and converts it into the consequent. Contraposition! Let's see if it works in this case. Contraposition says:

$$(p \supset q) \equiv (\sim q \supset \sim p)$$

Put in what you have:

$$? \equiv \sim(\sim E \supset F) \supset \sim(B \supset D)$$

You follow the rule and see what you can derive from it:

(B ⊃ D) ⊃ (~E ⊃ F) ≡ ~(~E ⊃ F) ⊃ ~(B ⊃ D)

1)	~(~E ⊃ F) ⊃ ~(B ⊃ D)	Premise
2)	F v D	Premise
3)	B ⊃ ~F	Premise
4)	(B ⊃ D) ⊃ (~E ⊃ F)	1, Contra
5)	~F ⊃ D	
6)	B ⊃ D	
7)	~E ⊃ F	
8)	E v F	

From what line was line 5 derived? Probably line 2. Which rule? Maybe DMI. If you are not sure, write out the rule, put in line 2 and see if you can derive line 5.

1)	~(~E ⊃ F) ⊃ ~(B ⊃ D)	Premise
2)	F v D	Premise
3)	B ⊃ ~F	Premise
4)	(B ⊃ D) ⊃ (~E ⊃ F)	1, Contra
5)	~F ⊃ D	2, DMI
6)	B ⊃ D	
7)	~E ⊃ F	
8)	E v F	

How about line 6? Maybe from line 4, but no rule seems to work. Look for all the rules with an "if...then" in the conclusion to see if you can find one that will work.

1)	~(~E ⊃ F) ⊃ ~(B ⊃ D)	Premise
2)	F v D	Premise
3)	B ⊃ ~F	Premise
4)	(B ⊃ D) ⊃ (~E ⊃ F)	1, Contra
5)	~F ⊃ D	2, DMI
6)	B ⊃ D	3, 5, CA
7)	~E ⊃ F	
8)	E v F	

Line 7? Well, it is the consequent of line 4. Can you find a rule that will enable you to get rid of the antecedent so you end up with the consequent all by itself? Look through all the "if...then" rules. Maybe Modus Ponens. But Modus Ponens has two premises so you need two lines. Maybe line 6. Let's try it and see if it works.

$$p \supset q$$
$$\underline{p \qquad\qquad}$$
$$q$$

Let's put in what we have:

$$(B \supset D) \supset (\sim E \supset F)$$
$$\underline{(B \supset D) \qquad\qquad\qquad\qquad}$$
$$?$$

1)	$\sim(\sim E \supset F) \supset \sim(B \supset D)$	Premise
2)	F v D	Premise
3)	$B \supset \sim F$	Premise
4)	$(B \supset D) \supset (\sim E \supset F)$	1, Contra
5)	$\sim F \supset D$	2, DMI
6)	$B \supset D$	3, 5, CA
7)	$\sim E \supset F$	4, 6, MP
8)	E v F	

How about the last line? Maybe from line 7. Which rule? Maybe DMI. If you are not sure, write out DMI, put in line 7 and see if you can derive line 8.

1)	$\sim(\sim E \supset F) \supset \sim(B \supset D)$	Premise
2)	F v D	Premise
3)	$B \supset \sim F$	Premise
4)	$(B \supset D) \supset (\sim E \supset F)$	1, Contra
5)	$\sim F \supset D$	2, DMI
6)	$B \supset D$	3, 5, CA
7)	$\sim E \supset F$	4, 6, MP
8)	E v F	7, DMI

Now these three examples are for kindergarten babies. If you are a lawyer arguing in court, your opponent is not going to present you with your argument all worked out so that all you have to do is say how it was derived. You will have to construct your own argument yourself. So enough of this kindergarten baby stuff. On to the real world where everyone has to construct their own arguments!

Consider this example:

1)	F ⊃ R	Premise
2)	R ⊃ ~E	Premise
3)	F	Premise
	Therefore, ~E	Conclusion

In this example, the first three lines are the premises and the last line is the conclusion. You are asked to construct an argument using the Rules of Inference that will enable you to derive the conclusion from these premises. You are to construct the argument below the black line.

Sometimes you can work backward from the conclusion in an attempt to discover an argument. Let's try it. You are looking for the conclusion, "~E". From what premise do you think you might be able to derive it? Probably from line 2 because it has a ~E in it. But you have to isolate the ~E by getting rid of the antecedent, R. Which rule will enable you to do that? Modus Ponens. But MP requires two premises. What other premise would you need in order to use MP? You would have to have an R by itself. So if you can figure out how to get an R by itself, you will be able to solve this problem.

From what line will you be able to get the R? Maybe from line 1. Which rule? MP. But MP requires two premises. What other line would you need? Yes, line 3. So you write down how you got the R, and then how you got the ~E.

1)	F ⊃ R	Premise
2)	R ⊃ ~E	Premise
3)	F	Premise
	Therefore, ~E	Conclusion
4)	R	1, 3, MP
5)	~E	2, 4, MP

You can also solve this problem by using CA and then MP.

Let's try another example:

1)	~(A • ~B)	Premise
2)	~B	Premise
3)	C ⊃ A	Premise
	Therefore, ~C	Conclusion

Below the black line, I am asked to construct an argument that will derive the conclusion from these premises. Let's try to work backward again. On these simple deductions, it usually works. (But on longer, more complicated deductions, you may not be able to work backward. You will just have to manipulate the premises in any way you can by using the Rules of Inference and hope that you bump into the conclusion by accident or serendipity.) From what line can I derive the conclusion, ~C? It has to be from the third premise because that is the only line with a C in it. How can I get a ~C from line 3? Look through all the "if...then" rules and maybe you'll find one. Well, if I had a ~A, I could use MT to get a ~C. So I can solve this problem if I can derive a ~A. Probably I will have to get the ~A from line 1. What rule would enable me to do that? Now I have to look through all the "and" rules. Maybe the Conjunctive Argument. But the Conjunctive Argument has two premises. All right, how about line 1 and line 2 and the Conjunctive Argument? Let's try it:

$$\frac{\begin{array}{c} \sim(p \bullet q) \\ q \end{array}}{\sim p}$$

Let's put in what I have and see what I can derive:

$$\frac{\begin{array}{c} \sim(A \bullet \sim B) \\ \sim B \end{array}}{?}$$

Does it work? Yes! So I solved the problem since I am able to drive a ~A.

1)	~(A • ~B)	Premise
2)	~B	Premise
3)	C ⊃ A	Premise
Therefore, ~C		Conclusion
4)	~A	1, 2, Conj. A
5)	~C	3, 4, MT

This is not the only way to prove this conclusion. There are a number of other ways:

1)	~(A • ~B)	Premise
2)	~B	Premise
3)	C ⊃ A	Premise
Therefore, ~C		Conclusion
4)	~A v B	1, DeM (or DMI)
5)	~A	4, 2, DA
6)	~C	3, 5, MT

Here is another way:

```
1)    ~(A • ~B)        Premise
2)    ~B               Premise
3)    C ⊃ A            Premise
Therefore, ~C          Conclusion
4)    A ⊃ B            1, DMI
5)    ~A               4, 2, MT
6)    ~C               3, 5, MT
```

Here is still another way:

```
1)    ~(A • ~B)        Premise
2)    ~B               Premise
3)    C ⊃ A            Premise
Therefore, ~C          Conclusion
4)    A ⊃ B            1, DMI
5)    C ⊃ B            3, 4, CA
6)    ~C               5, 2, MT
```

Try to do the following example by yourself. In this one, all you have to do is to indicate on the right side what line and what rule was used to derive each step of the argument. Kindergarten baby stuff!

```
1)    ~R ⊃ (S ⊃ T)     Premise
2)    ~(R v T)         Premise
3)    ~R • ~T
4)    ~R
5)    S ⊃ T
6)    ~T
7)    ~S
```

(Find the answer at the end of this section.

Here is an example where you yourself have to construct the argument. It takes a little more thought and a little more familiarity with the Rules of Inference. I am starting you out with an easy one so you will able to work backward to find the solution. Construct the argument below the black line.

```
1)  M ⊃ ~R         Premise
2)  R v V           Premise
3)  M               Premise
Therefore, V        Conclusion
```

Find the answer at the end of this section.

Answers:

1)	~R ⊃ (S ⊃ T)	Premise
2)	~(R v T)	Premise
3)	~R • ~T	2, DeM (or DMI)
4)	~R	3, Simp
5)	S ⊃ T	1, 4, MP
6)	~T	3, Simp
7)	~S	5, 6, MT

This next one has more than one answer.

1)	M ⊃ ~R	Premise
2)	R v V	Premise
3)	M	Premise
	Therefore, V	Conclusion

Let's try to work backward again. The conclusion has to come from line 2. So I am looking for a rule that will enable me to get rid of the R and end up with the V. Well, how about DA? But that needs two premises. To use DA, I would need not only line 2 but also a ~R. So I can solve this problem if I can derive a ~R. From where? It has to be from line 1. What rule will enable me to get a ~R from line one? So now I have to look through all the "if...then" rules. Maybe MP. But MP takes two premises. Oh, I've got the second premise in line 3! So:

1)	M ⊃ ~R	Premise
2)	R v V	Premise
3)	M	Premise
	Therefore, V	Conclusion
4)	~R	1, 3, MP
5)	V	2, 4, DA

Here's another way to do it:

1)	M ⊃ ~R	Premise
2)	R v V	Premise
3)	M	Premise
	Therefore, V	Conclusion
4)	~R ⊃ V	2, DMI
5)	~R	1, 3, MP
6)	V	4, 5, MT

And still another way:

1)	M ⊃ ~R	Premise
2)	R v V	Premise
3)	M	Premise
Therefore, V		Conclusion
4)	~R ⊃ V	2, DMI
5)	M ⊃ V	1, 4, CA
6)	V	5, 3, MP

And yet another:

1)	M ⊃ ~R	Premise
2)	R v V	Premise
3)	M	Premise
Therefore, V		Conclusion
4)	~M v ~R	1, DMI
5)	~R	4, 3, DA (or 1, 3, MP)
6)	V	2, 5 DA

And finally:

1)	M ⊃ ~R	Premise
2)	R v V	Premise
3)	M	Premise
Therefore, V		Conclusion
4)	~(M • R)	1, DMI
5)	~R	4, 3, Conj A
6)	V	2, 5, DA

Those are all the ways I know, but there may be more!

Exercise 10

A. <u>DIRECTIONS</u>: For each line after the premises, state from what previous line or lines it was derived and also state which rule was used to deduce it.

1. 1. p ⊃ q   premise
    2. r ⊃ p   premise
    3. r ⊃ q
    4. ~q ⊃ ~r

2. 1. q v (p • ~r)   premise
    2   ~q   premise
    3. p • ~r
    4. ~r

3. 1. p • q   premise
    2. q ⊃ r   premise
    3. q
    4. r

4. 1. (q • r) • p   premise
    2. (q • r) ⊃ s   premise
    3. q • r
    4. s

B. <u>DIRECTIONS</u>: Construct a deduction to prove that each of the following arguments is valid.

1. ~q • ~p, q v r, therefore, r.
2. p • q, ~(q • r), therefore, ~r.
3. ~p v q, r ⊃ p, therefore, r ⊃ q
4. p • s, r v r, therefore, s • r
5. r ⊃ s, ~s ⊃ s, therefore, s
6. p, r ⊃ q, ~(q • p), therefore, ~r
7. ~r v s, ~s v ~s, therefore, ~r
8. r ⊃ s, ~(p • ~p) ⊃ ~s, therefore, ~r
9. p, r ⊃ s, ~(s • p), therefore, ~r

C. <u>DIRECTIONS</u>: Symbolize each argument, then construct a deduction to prove its validity.

1. If Fiats are not reliable, then Mazdas are not reliable. Either Mazdas or Chevrolets are reliable. Fiats are not reliable. Therefore, Chevrolets must be reliable. (F, M, C)
2. Experimental treatment will be initiated if the patient's condition deteriorates. Either the patient's condition deteriorates or the patient improves. The patient does not improve. So experimental treatment will be initiated. (E, D, I)
3. If Steven comes for a visit, Nancy will be happy. If Nancy will be happy, then her parents will be happy. Her parents are not happy. So Steven does not come for a visit. (S, N, P)

Exercise 11

DIRECTIONS: In each of the following, state the justification for each line that is not a premise. State in each case what earlier lines are used and what rule applies.

1. 1.   J ⊃ (K • L)   Premise
    2.   J   Premise
    3.   K • L
    4.   K

2. 1.   (Q • R) ⊃ S   Premise
    2.   Q   Premise
    3.   R   Premise
    4.   Q • R
    5.   S

3. 1.   W ⊃ (X ⊃ Y)   Premise
    2.   W   Premise
    3.   ~Y   Premise
    4.   X ⊃ Y
    5.   ~X

4. 1.   A ⊃ B   Premise
    2.   B ⊃ C   Premise
    3.   C ⊃ D   Premise
    4.   A ⊃ C
    5.   A ⊃ D

DIRECTIONS: Construct deductions to establish validity. Another way to say "therefore" is by using the following symbol: "∴".

5. 1.   ~A ∨ ~C   Premise
    2.   C ∨ B   Premise
    3.   A   Premise
         ∴ B   Conclusion

6. 1.   J ⊃ K   Premise
    2.   L ∨ J   Premise
    3.   ~L   Premise
         ∴ K   Conclusion

7. 1.   Q ∨ R   Premise
    2.   Q ⊃ S   Premise
    3.   ~R   Premise
         ∴ S   Conclusion

8.   1.   X ∨ ~W   Premise
      2.   Y ⊃ W   Premise
      3.   ~X   Premise
          ∴ ~Y   Conclusion

9.   1.   C • E   Premise
      2.   D • C   Premise
      3.   ~E ∨ ~B   Premise
          ∴ A ∨ ~B   Conclusion

10.   1.   K ⊃ ~L   Premise
      2.   L ∨ J   Premise
      3.   K   Premise
          ∴ J • K   Conclusion

11.   1.   Q ⊃ ~(R • S)   Premise
      2.   Q • S   Premise
          ∴ ~R   Conclusion

Exercise 12

Use a truth table to test the validity of the argument or to answer the question.

1. If Shakespeare wrote both *Macbeth* and the *Iliad*, then he wrote the *Odyssey*. Therefore, if he did not write the *Odyssey*, then if he wrote *Macbeth* he did not write the *Iliad*. (M, I, O)

2. Is "If Juliet does not marry Paris then Romeo would be very happy," equivalent to "It's not the case that both Juliet will not marry Paris and Romeo would not be very happy"? (M, H)

3. You will pass the course if and only if you get down to work. Therefore, it is not the case that you will pass the course without getting down to work. (P, W)

4. If you use drugs or join a gang, then your parents will be distressed. But you do not use drugs. Therefore, if your parents are distressed, you have joined a gang. (D, G, P)

5. If you study both sculpture and painting, then you would like architecture. But you do not like architecture. Therefore, if you study sculpture, you do not study painting. (S, P, A)

6. Is "If Shakespeare wrote *Macbeth* and Homer wrote the *Iliad*, then Shakespeare did not write the *Odyssey*," equivalent to "If Shakespeare wrote *Macbeth*, then Homer wrote the *Iliad* only if Shakespeare did not write the *Odyssey*"? (M, I, O)

Chapter 3
Predicate Logic

Quantification

Consider the following syllogism:

> All humans are mortal.
> Socrates is human.
> Therefore, Socrates is mortal.

How would you symbolize this argument? Well, you could not symbolize it because you have not learned about quantification yet. Quantification enables you to translate categorical sentences into the language of symbolic logic. So let's begin with the quantifiers. There are two quantifiers along with their negations.

1) Here is the "universal quantifier": (x).

2) Here is the "existential quantifier": (∃x).

In English, here is the meaning of these quantifiers along with their negations:

(x):	Given anything whatever...
~(x):	Not everything is such that...
(∃x):	There is at least one thing such that...
~(∃x):	There is not even one thing such that...

Consider the following examples:

A: (x)Mx

The universal quantifier is in parenthesis (as are all the quantifiers). Let's say that "M" stands for "mortal". The "x" after the "M" refers to the thing that the quantifier is quantifying. We translate the symbolic sentence, (x)Mx, in the following way: Given anything whatever (referring the quantifier), that thing (referring to the x following the M) is mortal (referring to the M). So "Given anything whatever, that thing is mortal" says, "Everything is mortal".

I know that it is easier to say it the short way: "Everything is mortal". But I want you always to say it the long way: "Given anything whatever, that thing is mortal". Eventually things will get more complicated and you are going to get lost if you say it the short way. SO SAY EVERYTHING THE LONG WAY!

E: (x)~Mx

The long way: Given anything whatever, that thing is not mortal.

The short way: Nothing is mortal.

I: (∃x)Mx

There is at least one thing such that, that thing is mortal.

Something is mortal.

O: (∃x)~Mx

There is at least one thing such that, that thing is not mortal.

Something is not mortal.

To summarize:

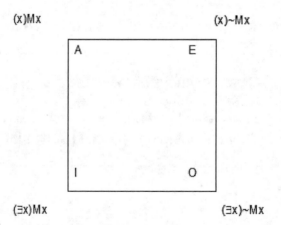

Subject-Predicate Propositions

A: All S are P.
     This is symbolized:
        (x)(Sx ⊃ Px)

In English this symbolic sentence says:

Given anything whatever (referring to the quantifier), if (referring to ⊃) that thing (referring to the x following the S) is S (referring to the S), then (referring to ⊃) that thing (referring to the x following the P) is P (referring to the P). So, "Given anything whatever, if that thing is S, then that thing is P".

E: No S are P
> (x)(Sx ⊃ ~Px)
>> Given anything whatever, if that thing is S then that thing is not P.

I: Some S are P
> (∃x)(Sx • Px)
>> There is at least one thing such that, that thing is S and that thing is P.

O: Some S are not P
> (∃x)(Sx • ~Px)
>> There is at least one thing such that, that thing is S and that thing is not P.

To summarize:

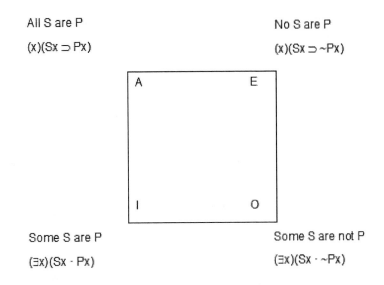

OK, so now we can get back to our syllogism at the beginning of Chapter 3:

> All humans are mortal.
> Socrates is human.
> Therefore, Socrates is mortal.

We have all the information necessary to symbolize it. For "All humans are mortal" follow the "A" sentence pattern in the square above: (x)(Hx ⊃ Mx). Now consider the second premise, "Socrates is human". In this sentence, we are talking about a specific person, Socrates, rather than about humans in general. So we do not use an "x" (which stands for any human); instead we can use an "s" since we are talking about "Socrates". So the second premise is symbolized: Hs. The conclusion is symbolized following the pattern of the second premise. So this is what it would look like:

$$\frac{\begin{array}{l}(x)(Hx \supset Mx) \\ Hs \end{array}}{Ms}$$

Why would it be wrong to symbolize the first premise: "(x)(Hx • Mx)"? In other words, what does "(x)(Hx • Mx)" mean? Say it out the long way and you will hear the problem. It says: "Given anything whatever, that thing is human and that thing is mortal". It says that everything in the whole world (cats, dogs, trees, and mountains) is human and mortal. That is not what the "A" sentence says. The "A" sentence says, "All humans are mortal". <u>So if you want a categorical sentence: whenever you use the universal quantifier you must use the "if...then" symbol</u> (rather than the "and" symbol).

Why would it be wrong to symbolize "Some humans are mortal" as: "(∃x)(Hx ⊃ Mx)"? Say it out the long way and you will hear why it is wrong. It says, "There is at least one thing, such that if that thing is human, then that thing is mortal". This sentence does not assert existence. It merely says "**if** there is a human" then he is also mortal. Remember that "some" in logic means "at least one" is in existence! So (∃x)(Hx ⊃ Mx) is not a categorical sentence because it does not assert existence. (It is merely a hypothetical sentence.) <u>If you want a categorical sentence: whenever you use the existential quantifier, you must use the "and" symbol</u> (rather than the "if...then" symbol).

The Square of Opposition

Let's consider the relationship between the "A" and the "O" sentence, and the relationship between the "E" and the "I" sentence. This relationship is called "<u>contradictories</u>".

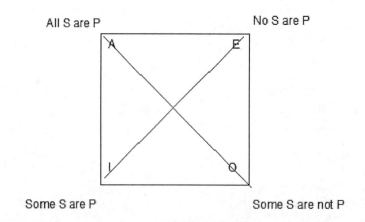

Let's say that "All S are P" stands for "All Southerners are Protestant". If we know that "All Southerners are Protestant" is true, what can we say about the "O" sentence, "Some Southerners are not Protestant"? It must be false.

If we know that "Some Southerners are not Protestant" is true, what can we say about the "A" sentence, "All Southerners are Protestant"? It must be false.

If we know that the "E" sentence is true, what can we say about the "I" sentence? It must be false.

If we know that the "I" sentence is true, what can we say about the "E" sentence? It must be false.

So that is the nature of contradictories: If one is true, the other must be false; if one is false, the other must be true.

So based on the nature of contradictories, we can say that the "A" sentence is equivalent to the negation of the "O" sentence. The "E" sentence is equivalent to the negation of the "I" sentence. The "I" sentence is equivalent to the negation of the "E" sentence. And the "O" sentence is equivalent to the negation of the "A" sentence.

Quantificational Equivalences (QE)

Based on the nature of contradictories, we can be certain that the following chart is correct:

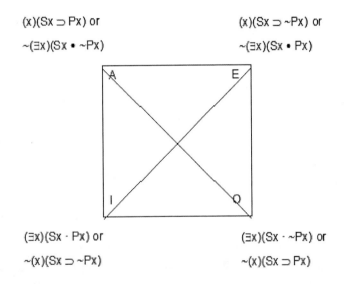

$(x)(Sx \supset Px)$ or $(x)(Sx \supset {\sim}Px)$ or

$\sim(\exists x)(Sx \bullet {\sim}Px)$ $\sim(\exists x)(Sx \bullet Px)$

$(\exists x)(Sx \cdot Px)$ or $(\exists x)(Sx \cdot {\sim}Px)$ or

$\sim(x)(Sx \supset {\sim}Px)$ $\sim(x)(Sx \supset Px)$

We can summarize the information in the above square of opposition in the following handy chart of Quantificational Equivalences (QE) for subject-predicate propositions:

$$(x)(Sx \supset Px) \quad \equiv \quad \sim(\exists x)(Sx \bullet {\sim}Px)$$
$$(x)(Sx \supset {\sim}Px) \quad \equiv \quad \sim(\exists x)(Sx \bullet Px)$$
$$(\exists x)(Sx \cdot Px) \quad \equiv \quad \sim(x)(Sx \supset {\sim}Px)$$
$$(\exists x)(Sx \cdot {\sim}Px) \quad \equiv \quad \sim(x)(Sx \supset Px)$$

You know how to translate into English the negation of the quantifiers. You know how to translate into English the negation within the parentheses. But we have not yet considered a negation outside of the parentheses, for example, (x)~(Sx ⊃ Px). It says, "Given anything whatever, it is not the case that if that thing is an S then that thing is a P". It is rather difficult to understand the meaning of that English sentence. It cannot mean "No S are P" because "No S are P" is symbolized (x)(Sx ⊃ ~Px). The best way to translate (x)~(Sx ⊃ Px) into understandable English is to manipulate it by the Rules of Inference until the English becomes intelligible. For example:

1)   (x)~(Sx ⊃ Px)
2)   (x)~(~Sx v Px)   1, DMI
3)   (x)(Sx • ~Px)   2, DeM (or DMI).

Line 3 is pretty easy to understand in English: "Everything is S and non-P". It is perfectly acceptable to say that if you want to, but it just is not a categorical sentence.

Based on the nature of contradictories, we can also be certain that the following Quantificational Equivalences (QE) are correct:

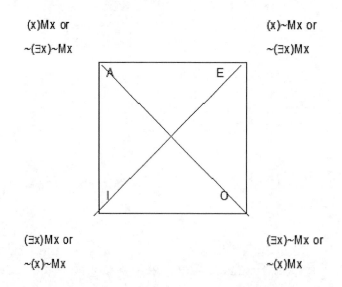

(x)Mx or

~(∃x)~Mx

(x)~Mx or

~(∃x)Mx

(∃x)Mx or

~(x)~Mx

(∃x)~Mx or

~(x)Mx

A: (x)Mx ≡ ~(∃x)~Mx.

~(∃x)~Mx says: "There is not even one thing such that that thing is not mortal".

So (x)Mx, "Everything is mortal" means the same as ~(∃x)~Mx, "Nothing is not mortal".

E: (x)~Mx ≡ ~(∃x)Mx

~(∃x)Mx says: "There is not even one thing such that that thing is mortal".

"Everything is not mortal" is equivalent to "Nothing is mortal".

I: $(\exists x)Mx \equiv \sim(x)\sim Mx$

$\sim(x)\sim Mx$ says: "Not everything is such that that thing is not mortal".

"Something is mortal" is equivalent to "Not everything is not mortal".

O: $(\exists x)\sim Mx \equiv \sim(x)Mx$

$\sim(x)Mx$ says: "Not everything is such that that thing is mortal".

"Something is not mortal" is equivalent to "Not everything is mortal".

We can summarize all this in the following handy chart of Quantificational Equivalences (QE), which you can find in the Rules of Inference:

$(x)Mx$	$\equiv$	$\sim(\exists x)\sim Mx$
$(x)\sim Mx$	$\equiv$	$\sim(\exists x)Mx$
$(\exists x)Mx$	$\equiv$	$\sim(x)\sim Mx$
$(\exists x)\sim Mx$	$\equiv$	$\sim(x)Mx$

Look at the second half of the *first line* of the above chart of QE. It says: "$\sim(\exists x)\sim Mx$". Here is another way to derive its equivalence:

1) Move the first negation to the right through the quantifier.

2) The quantifier changes its symbol, in this case from existential to universal.

3) And the negation comes out on the opposite side of the changed quantifier.

4) So we get: $(x)\sim\sim Mx$, which is equivalent to $(x)Mx$.

We can also move the negation to the left. Look at the second half of *third line* of the above chart of QE. It says: $\sim(x)\sim Mx$. To derive its equivalence:

1) Move the second negation to the left through the quantifier.

2) The quantifier changes it symbol, in this case, from universal to existential.

3) And the negation comes out on the other side of the new quantifier.

So we get: $\sim\sim(\exists x)Mx$, which is equivalent to $(\exists x)Mx$.

Exercise 14

A. <u>DIRECTIONS</u>: Match each of the following sentences with its appropriate symbolic formulation.

1. Everything is material.

    a. ~(∃x) (x is spiritual)

2. Something is material.

    b. (∃y) (y is material)

3. Nothing is spiritual.

    c. (x)(x is material)

4. Everything is both material and spiritual.

    d. ~(x) (x is spiritual)

5. Everything is either material or spiritual.

    e. (y)(y is not material • y is not spiritual)

6. Everything is neither material nor spiritual.

    f. (x)(x is material • x is spiritual)

7. Not everything is spiritual.

    g. (x)(x is material v x is spiritual)

8. Something is either material or spiritual.

    h. (x)(x is spiritual) ⊃ ~(∃x)(x is material)

9. Something is material but everything is spiritual.

    i. (x)(x is material) • (∃x) (x is spiritual)

10. Everything is material, but only some things are spiritual.

    j. (∃x)(x is material) • (x)(x is spiritual)

11. If everything is material, then nothing is spiritual.

    k. (∃y)(y is material v y is spiritual)

12. If everything is spiritual, then nothing is material.

    l. (x) (x is material) ⊃ ~(∃x) (x is spiritual)

B. <u>DIRECTIONS</u>: Symbolize each of the following sentences. Use "R" to mean "is red" and "W" to mean "is white".

1. Something is red.

2. Something is not red.

3. Everything is red.

4. Nothing is red.

5. Not everything is red.

6. Something is both red and white.

7. Something is red but not white.

8. If everything is red, then nothing is white.

9. If something is white, then not everything is red.

10. It is not the case that something is both red and white.

C. <u>DIRECTIONS</u>: Translate each of the following sentences into English. Which sentences are true? Which sentences are false? Which contain free variables?

(The mortal sin of quantification is a variable [like "x" or "y"] that is unquantified or "free". Every variable must be quantified with either the universal quantifier or the existential quantifier. Please, no mortal sins in this class!)

1. (x) (x is timeless v x is dated).
2. (y) (y is timeless • y is dated).
3. (y) (y is timeless) • z is dated.
4. (z) (z is timeless) • z is dated.
5. (x) (x is dated) ⊃ ~(∃y) (y is timeless).
6. (∃x) (x is timeless) ⊃ (y) (y is dated).
7. y is timeless v y is dated.
8. x is timeless • (∃y) (y is dated).
9. (∃y) (y is timeless) • z is dated.

Exercise 15

Translate the following categorical sentences into quantificational symbolism. Let "Bx" = "x is a Baptist," "Cx" = "x is conservative," "Ux" = "x is a Unitarian," and "Px" = "x is progressive."

1. Some Baptists are conservative and some Unitarians are progressive.
2. If some Baptists are not conservative, then not all Baptists are conservative.
3. If some Unitarians are conservative, then it is not the case that all Unitarians are progressive.
4. Not every Baptist is conservative and not every Unitarian is progressive.
5. No Unitarians are conservative if and only if no Baptists are progressive.
6. Some Baptists are progressive only if some Unitarians are conservative.
7. Either some Baptists are not progressive or some Unitarians are not conservative.
8. If all Unitarians are progressive, then all Baptists are conservative.
9. All Unitarians are progressive only if not one Unitarian is conservative.
10. If not every Baptist is conservative, then some Baptists are progressive.
11. If some Baptists are progressive, then both Baptists and Unitarians are progressive.
12. If some Baptists are progressive, then either no Unitarians are progressive or some progressives are not Unitarians.

Exercise 16

A. <u>DIRECTIONS</u>: Translate each of the three possible answers into English the long way. Pick the one that is the correct answer. Assume "S" means "is a squirrel" and "C" means "can fly".

1. All squirrels can fly.
    a. (x) Sx ⊃ Cx
    b. (x) (Sx • Cx)
    c. (z) (Sz ⊃ Cz)

2. No squirrels can fly.
    a. ~(x) (Sx ⊃ Cx)
    b. ~(∃x) Sx • Cx
    c. (y) (Sy ⊃ ~Cy)

3. Some squirrels can fly.
    a. (∃x) (Sx ⊃ Cx)
    b. (∃x) Sx • Cx
    c. ~(x) (Sx ⊃ ~Cx)

4. Some squirrels cannot fly.
    a. ~(x) (Sx ⊃ Cx)
    b. (∃z) (Sz ⊃ ~Cz)
    c. (∃x) (Sy • ~Cy)

B. <u>DIRECTIONS</u>: Translate the following symbolic sentences into English the long way. Indicate whether each is an A , E, I, or O sentence. Assume "A" means "is an American", "E" means "is an environmentalist", and "P" means "is patriotic".

1.	(x) (Ex ⊃ Px)	6.	(x) (~Px ⊃ ~Ex)
2.	(∃x) (Ax • Px)	7.	~(∃x) (Px • ~Ax)
3.	~(x) (Ax ⊃ Ex)	8.	~(∃x) (Ex • Ax)
4.	(∃x) (Ax • ~Px)	9.	(∃x) (~Ex • ~Px)
5.	~(x) (Px ⊃ ~Ax)	10.	~(∃x) (~Ax • Px)

C. <u>DIRECTIONS</u>: Symbolize each of the following sentences using the appropriate quantifier. Let "I" mean "is an idealist", "R" mean "is a romanticist", and "A" mean "is an abstractionist".

1. Some idealists are not romanticists.

2. No abstractionists are idealists.

3. Not all non-romanticists are abstractionists.

4. All abstractionists are non-romanticists.

5. Some non-romanticists are idealists.

6. No romantic idealists are abstractionists.

7. All abstractionists are idealistic romanticists.

8. There is not even one idealist who is a romantic abstractionist.

9. Some idealistic abstractionists are romanticists.

10. Some romantic abstractionists are not non-idealistic.

Quantificational Inference Rules

Let's get back to the syllogism that we were considering at the beginning of this chapter. We have yet to prove its validity.

> All human are mortal.
> Socrates is human.
> Therefore, Socrates is mortal.

We already know how to symbolize it:

> 1. $(x)(Hx \supset Mx)$
> 2. Hs
> Therefore, Ms

In order to prove the validity of arguments involving quantification, we need to add four additional rules to our Rules of Inference. The first is called the <u>RULE OF UNIVERSAL INSTANTIATION (UI)</u>. It says: From any universally quantified statement, we may validly deduce any instance of it.

Using UI along with our other Rules of Inference, we can prove the validity of the above syllogism:

1.	$(x)(Hx \supset Mx)$	Premise
2.	Hs	Premise
Therefore, Ms		Conclusion
3.	$Hs \supset Ms$	1, UI
4.	Ms	3,2, MP

Here is the reason that we need the Rule of Universal Instantiation (UI). Line 1, $(x)(Hx \supset Mx)$, is not a compound sentence. It may look like a compound sentence because it has an antecedent and a consequent contained within it, but it is actually a <u>categorical</u> sentence. The Rules of Inference work only on <u>compound</u> sentences. So we have to transform line 1 into a compound sentence before we can use the Rules of Inference on it. UI enables us to transform categorical sentences into compound sentences.

Let's try to prove the validity of another syllogism. How about this second example:

> All humans are mortal.
> All Greeks are human.
> Therefore, all Greeks are mortal.

First we symbolize it, then we use UI to convert the premises from categorical sentences to compound sentences. That will enable us to use our Rules of Inference. In the previous example, when we instantiated, we knew the actual name of the person we were talking about: Socrates. So we used an "s" when we instantiated to symbolize "Socrates". In this example, we do not know the actual name of the person or persons we are instantiating. So we will use "a" to symbolize "any arbitrarily selected individual".

If we can say something about an entire set of people, then we can say the same thing about "any arbitrarily selected individual" within that set. In other words, if we can say something about an entire set, we can say the same thing about any member of that set.

1.	(x)(Hx ⊃ Mx)	Premise
2.	(x)(Gx ⊃ Hx)	Premise
Therefore, (x)(Gx ⊃ Mx)		Conclusion
3.	Ha ⊃ Ma	1, UI
4.	Ga ⊃ Ha	2, UI
5.	Ga ⊃ Ma	4, 3, CA

Now line 5 is pretty close to our conclusion. It is a compound sentence, however, we are looking for a categorical sentence. So now we need a rule to transform a compound sentence into a categorical sentence that is universal. That rule is called the RULE OF UNIVERSAL GENERALIZATION (UG). It says: From an instance, which is true of any arbitrarily selected individual, we may infer the universal quantification. In other words, if you can say something about any individual member of a set, then you can say that same thing about every member of that set. So by using UG, we can derive our conclusion.

6.   (x)(Gx ⊃ Mx)   5, UG

Let's try a third example. Consider the following syllogism:

All Cretans are virtuous.
Some humans are Cretans.
Therefore, some humans are virtuous.

1.	(x)(Cx ⊃ Vx)	Premise
2.	(∃x)(Hx • Cx)	Premise
Therefore, (∃x)(Hx • Vx)		Conclusion

This example presents a new problem. Line 2 begins with an existential quantifier. So we need an additional rule in order to instantiate it. This rule is called the <u>RULE OF EXISTENTIAL INSTANTIATION (EI)</u>. It says: From any existentially quantified statement, we may deduce any instance of it provided that the name being introduced (e.g. "a", "b", "c") is one that has not been previously used in the deduction. Using this new rule we derive:

1.	(x)(Cx $\supset$ Vx)	Premise
2.	($\exists$x)(Hx • Cx)	Premise
Therefore, ($\exists$x)(Hx • Vx)		Conclusion
3.	Ha • Ca	2, EI
4.	Ca $\supset$ Va	1, UI
5.	Ha	3, Simp
6.	Ca	3, Simp
7.	Va	4, 6, MP
8.	Ha • Va	5, 7, Conj.

Pretty close to our conclusion, except now we need an additional rule that converts a compound sentence into a categorical sentence that is particular. This rule is called: the <u>RULE OF EXISTENTIAL GENERALIZATION (EG)</u>. It says: From a true instance we may infer the existential quantification. In other words, if we know that one human being is virtuous, we can say, "Some humans are virtuous". Using this rule, we can derive our conclusion.

9.	($\exists$x)(Hx • Vx)	8, EG

Let's try this fourth and final example:
Some alligators are contentious.
Some birds are contentious.
Therefore, some alligators are birds.

1.	($\exists$x)(Ax • Cx)	Premise
2.	($\exists$x)(Bx • Cx)	Premise
Therefore, ($\exists$x)(Ax • Bx)		Conclusion
3.	Aa • Ca	1, EI
4.	Ba • Ca	2, EI
5.	Aa	3, Simp
6.	Ba	4, Simp
7.	Aa • Ba	5, 6 Conj.
8.	($\exists$x)(Ax • Bx)	7, EG

Look what we proved by using these infallible Rules of Inference. We proved that "Some alligators are birds"! What? That's ridiculous. So where did we go wrong?

Find the answer at the end of this section. But first reread the four quantificational inference rules, then think about it for a minute before you look at the answer.

Answer:

We disobeyed EI on line 4. EI says: From any existentially quantified statement, we may deduce any instance of it <u>provided that the name being introduced</u> (e.g. "a", "b", "c") <u>is one that has not been previously used in the deduction</u>. In line 4, we introduced "a" for the second time. Were we to do line 4 correctly, it would have to be "Bb • Cb". But then we would not be able to deduce the conclusion. Of course, we would not be able to deduce the conclusion because the argument is invalid! If you do not follow EI correctly, then you will end up proving invalid arguments. "Proving an invalid argument" is clearly an oxymoron. (An oxymoron is a combination of contradictory words, like "If you have a gas leak, the next morning you just might wake up dead!"). SO HERE IS THE MORAL OF THE STORY: if you have to use both EI and UI in the same argument as we did in the third example above, then <u>you must use EI before you use UI</u>. EI says you cannot introduce a name that has been previously used in the argument. UI, however, has no such restriction. Using UI, you can introduce the same name as many times as you like in an argument.

Exercise 17

DIRECTIONS: Construct a formal proof of validity for each of the following arguments, in each case, using the suggested notation.

1. No atheists are believers. Carlos is a believer. Therefore, Carlos is not an atheist. (Ax, Bx, c)

2. All dramatists are emotional. Some philosophers are not emotional. Therefore, some philosophers are not dramatists. (Dx, Ex, Px)

3. No golfers are neurotic. Some psychologists are neurotic. Therefore, some psychologists are not golfers. (Gx, Px, Nx)

4. All writers are drinkers. No drinkers are happy. Therefore, no writers are happy. (Wx, Dx, Hx)

5. All philosophers are rational. Some dramatists are philosophers. Therefore, some dramatists are rational. (Px, Rx, Dx)

The Logic of Relations

We can extend our symbolism in two ways. First, in order to symbolize relations between things, we can use a capital letter followed by more than one variable. For example, "Lxy" says, "x loves y" or the same thing in different words, "y is loved by x". "Lyx" says "y loves x" or "x is loved by y".

Secondly, we can allow one quantifier to occur within the scope of another. For example:

 a) (∃x)(∃y)Lxy

There is at least one thing [symbolized by (∃x)] such that that thing [symbolized by second x] loves [symbolized by L] at least one [symbolized by (∃y)] other thing [symbolized by the second y].

 Something loves something.

 b) (x)(y)Lxy

Given anything whatever [(x)], that thing [the second x] loves [L] everything [(y)] (including itself).

 Everything loves everything.

 c) (x)(∃y)Lxy

Given anything whatever [(x)], that thing [the second x] loves [L] at least one [(∃y)] thing [the second y].

 Everything loves something.

 d) (∃x)(y)Lxy

There is at least one thing [(∃x)] such that it [the second x] loves [L] everything [(y)].

 Something loves everything.

What do these say?

 1) (∃x)Lxx

 2) (x)Lxx

Find the answers at the end of this section.

Answers:

1. There is at least one thing such that it loves itself.
    Something loves itself.

2. Given anything whatever, it loves itself.
    Everything loves itself.

Speaking About Persons

So far we have been talking about things. But we also can extend the logic of relations to talk about persons. Let's say that "P" stands for "person" and "L" stands for "love".

> 1) $(\exists x)[Px \bullet (\exists y)(Py \bullet Lxy)]$

There is at least one thing [$(\exists x)$] such that that thing is a person [Px] and [$\bullet$] there is at least one other thing [$(\exists y)$] such that the second thing is a person [Py] and [$\bullet$] the first thing loves the second thing [Lxy)].

> Someone loves someone.

> 2) $(x)[Px \supset (y)(Py \supset Lxy)]$

Given anything whatever [(x)], if [$\supset$] it is a person [Px] then [$\supset$] given any other thing whatever [(y)], if [$\supset$] the second thing is a person [Py] then [$\supset$] the first thing loves the second thing [Lxy].

> Everyone loves everyone.

> 3) $(x)[Px \supset (\exists y)(Py \bullet Lxy)]$

Given anything whatever, if it is a person then there is at least one thing such that the second thing is a person and the first thing loves the second thing.

> Everyone loves someone.

> 4) $(\exists x)[Px \bullet (y)(Py \supset Lxy)]$

There is at least one thing such that it is a person and given anything whatever, if the second thing is a person then the first thing loves it.

> Someone loves everyone.

Active and Passive Voice

The order of the quantifiers can affect the meaning of the sentence:

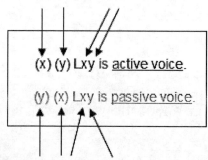

If the sequence of the quantifiers is (x)(y) and the sequence of the variables is x, y, then the sentence is active voice.

If the quantifiers are (y)(x) and the variables are in reverse order [x, y], then the sentence is passive voice.

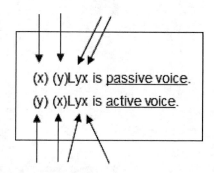

If the quantifiers are (x)(y) and the variables are in reverse order [y, x], then the sentence is passive voice.

If the order of the quantifiers is (y)(x) and the order of the variables is in the same order [y, x], then the sentence is active voice.

    a)   (x)(y)Lxy $\equiv$ Everything loves everything.   [Active voice]
        But (y)(x)Lxy says:
                Given anything whatever, it is loved by given
                anything whatever.
                Everything is loved by everything.
                (y)(x)Lxy $\equiv$ (x)(y)Lyx   [Passive voice]

b) (x)(∃y)Lxy ≡ Everything loves something.   [Active voice]
    But (∃y)(x)Lxy says:
        There is at least one thing such that it is loved by
        given anything whatever.
        Something is loved by everything.
        (∃y)(x)Lxy ≡ (∃x)(y)Lyx   [Passive voice]

c) (∃x)(y)Lxy ≡ Something loves everything.   [Active voice]
    But (y)(∃x)Lxy says:
        Given anything whatever, it is loved by at least
        one thing.
        Everything is loved by something.
        (y)(∃x)Lxy ≡ (x)(∃y)Lyx   [Passive voice]

d) (∃x)(∃y)Lxy ≡ Something loves something.   [Active voice]
    But (∃y)(∃x)Lxy says:
        There is at least one thing such that it is loved by
        at least one thing.
        Something is loved by something.
        (∃y)(∃x)Lxy ≡ (∃x)(∃y)Lyx   [Passive voice]

Let's summarize what we have learned so far with the following chart:

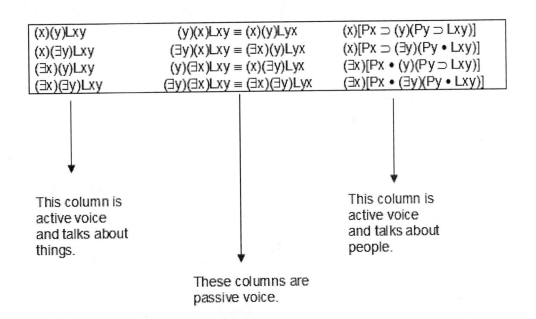

(x)(y)Lxy	(y)(x)Lxy ≡ (x)(y)Lyx	(x)[Px ⊃ (y)(Py ⊃ Lxy)]
(x)(∃y)Lxy	(∃y)(x)Lxy ≡ (∃x)(y)Lyx	(x)[Px ⊃ (∃y)(Py • Lxy)]
(∃x)(y)Lxy	(y)(∃x)Lxy ≡ (x)(∃y)Lyx	(∃x)[Px • (y)(Py ⊃ Lxy)]
(∃x)(∃y)Lxy	(∃y)(∃x)Lxy ≡ (∃x)(∃y)Lyx	(∃x)[Px • (∃y)(Py • Lxy)]

This column is
active voice
and talks about
things.

These columns are
passive voice.

This column is
active voice
and talks about
people.

More Complication

Try to symbolize this example: "Good men always have friends". Since we are dealing with quantification, both "good men" and "friends" have to be quantified. So before we symbolize it, we have to rewrite the original sentence in English so that it includes quantification for both the subject term and the predicate term: "All good men have some friends". Now the sentence is ready for us to symbolize. Let's say that G stands for "good", M stands for "men", and F stands for "friends".

All good men have some friends.

(x)[(Gx • Mx) ⊃ (∃y)Fyx] says:

"Given anything whatever, if that thing is good and that thing is a man, then there is at least one other thing such that the first thing is befriended by the second thing."

Please note that this example, "All good men have some friends", does <u>not</u> say: (x)[(Gx • Mx) ⊃ (∃y)Fxy]. This says something quite different. It says, "All good men are friends to some persons".

Let's try another example: "Bad men never have friends". First, quantify "bad men" and "friends". Try to do it yourself before you look at the next sentence. No cheating! The revised sentence would be: "<u>No</u> bad men have <u>any</u> friends".

(x)[(Bx • Mx) ⊃ ~(∃y)Fyx] says:

"Given anything whatever, if that thing is bad and that thing is a man, then not even one thing is such that the first thing is befriended by the second thing."

Or by QE:

[(x)[(Bx • Mx) ⊃ (y)~Fyx]]

Consider another example: "No one in this class is related to everyone in this class". This statement is probably true. It would be hard to find a single person in our class that is related to each and every other student in the class. You would probably have to go all the way back to Adam and Eve for this one to be true. We would symbolize this statement as:

~(∃x) {(Px • Cx) • (y)[(Py • Cy) ⊃ Rxy]}

If we simplified this statement to speak only about things, it would say, "Nothing is related to everything", symbolized ~(∃x)(y)Rxy.

Here is a completely different statement: "No one in the class is related to <u>anyone</u> in this class". Now this is a lot less likely to be true. I have had a father and son in my class. I have had a mother and daughter. And I have had two sisters. And I have had a man and wife. So this statement is quite different from the previous one and can be symbolized:

~(∃x){(Px • Cx) • (∃y)[(Py • Cy) • Rxy]}

If we simplified it to speak only about things, it would say, "Nothing is related to <u>anything</u>", symbolized

~(∃x)(∃y)Rxy

Next consider the statement "Something loves <u>anything</u>", which would be symbolized

(∃x)(y) Lxy

Well, it is all very interesting, you say, but what is the moral of the story? HERE IS THE MORAL OF THE STORY: Whenever you see the word "nothing", you have no problem because you are always going to symbolize it: ~(∃x). For example, "<u>Nothing</u> loves something" is symbolized ~(∃x)(∃y)Lxy.

Whenever you see the words "not everything", you have no problem because you are always going to symbolize it: ~(x). For example, "<u>Not everything</u> loves everything" is symbolized ~(x)(y)Lxy.

But when you see the word "anything", you've got a problem because in the examples above we have not always symbolize "anything" in the same way. In one example, "Nothing is related to <u>anything</u>", we symbolized the word "anything" as

In another example, "Something loves <u>anything</u>", we symbolized the word "anything" as

"(y)"

In one example, we used the existential quantifier; in the other example, we used the universal quantifier.

As if the logic of relations were not already complicated enough, why do we have this added complication with the word "anything"? At the risk of total confusion, I will attempt to explain it! Let's say your rich uncle comes for a visit. He says he is going to buy you dinner at the best restaurant in town. He leaves it up to you to choose the restaurant. You tell him frankly, "To save your soul, it is impossible to get a good meal in this town; but there is a little town up the coast that has many fine restaurants". He says, "Let's go!" So the two of you drive up Pacific Coast Highway to Santa Barbara. You choose a fancy restaurant by the beach, just in time to watch a glorious sunset. When you finally get seated in a cozy corner, your uncle says, "Oh, I almost forgot. I have a very important business telephone call to make, but it will only take me a few minutes. In the mean time, order anything you want." Then he runs off to make his phone call.

When he comes back, he does not expect you to have ordered everything on the menu! He meant for you to order a few of the things you really like, for instance, a cocktail, a salad, an entrée of maybe fish or meat, and a dessert. In this case, "anything" means "some" of the things you really like.

Now consider another example. The television actor, Don Knotts, used to play the part of a sheriff who was very nervous. Whenever he had to draw his revolver in the line of duty, he would be so nervous that his revolver would shake. As a result, he did not appear to be very authoritative, but instead appeared to be rather silly. You might say about someone like that, "He is afraid of anything!" In this case, "anything" means "everything".

There is the problem. The meaning of the word "anything" depends on the context in which it is used. So when you are trying to symbolize the word "anything", always say the symbols out the long way because then you are much more likely to hear the real meaning. If you say the symbols the short way, you will get the "anythings" wrong.

Here is a method that might enable you to check your symbolization to see if it is correct. Use QE to derive an equivalent symbolization that may be easier for you to translate into English. Here is an example of QE:

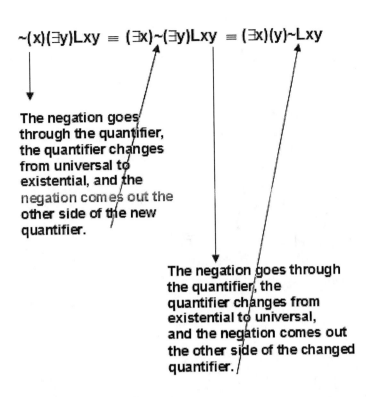

~(x)(∃y)Lxy means "Not everything is such that that thing loves at least one other thing" or "Not everyone loves someone".

(∃x)~(∃y)Lxy means "There is at least one thing such that that thing loves not even one thing" or "Someone loves nobody".

(∃x)(y)~Lxy means "There is at least one thing such that that thing does not love given anything whatever" or "Someone does not love anyone".

Exercise 18

DIRECTIONS: Symbolize the following sentences, using "Hxy" as short for "country x helps country y".

1. Every country helps every country.
2. Some country helps at least one country.
3. Each country helps itself.
4. At least one country helps itself.
5. At least one country helps every country.
6. Every country is helped by some country.
7. Some country is helped by every country.
8. Each country helps at least one country.
9. At least one country helps any country.
10. There is no country that helps any other country.

Exercise 19

DIRECTIONS: Translate each of the following sentences into symbolic form.

PART A
1. Something frightens something.
2. Everything frightens everything.
3. Everything is frightened by something.
4. Everything frightens something.
5. Nothing frightens everything.
6. Nothing frightens no thing.
7. Nothing frightens anything.
8. Something does not frighten everything.
9. Something does not frighten anything.

PART B
1. Someone frightens someone.
2. Everyone frightens everyone.
3. Everyone is frightened by someone.
4. Everyone frightens someone.
5. No one frightens everyone.
6. No one frightens no one.
7. No one frightens anyone.
8. Someone does not frighten everyone.
9. Someone does not frighten anyone.

Exercise 20

A. <u>DIRECTIONS</u>: Symbolize the following sentences according to the logic of relations. Use "Lxy" for "x loves y".

1. Everything loves something.

2. Something loves everything.

3. Everything is loved by something.

4. Something is loved by everything.

5. Something loves anything.

6. Something loves itself.

7. Nothing loves everything.

8. Something loves nothing.

9. Something does not love anything.

10. Anything loves something.

B. <u>DIRECTIONS</u>: Translate the following symbolic sentences into English the long way. Assume "B" means "is a blond", "L" means "is Latin", and "A" means "adores".

1. (x)(Bx ⊃ ~Lx)

2. (∃x)(Lx • Bx)

3. (∃x)[Lx • (y)(By ⊃ Axy)]

4. (x)[Lx ⊃ (∃y)(By • Axy)]

5. ~(∃x)[Lx • (y)(By ⊃ Axy)]

6. (∃x)[Lx • (∃y)(By • Axy)]

7. (y)[Ly ⊃ (x)(Bx ⊃ Ayx)]

8. (∃x)[Bx • (y)(Ly ⊃ Ayx)]

9. (x)[Bx ⊃ (∃y)(Ly • Ayx)]

10. ~(∃y)[By • (x)(Lx ⊃ Axy)]

Conditional Proof

Let's begin our study of conditional proof with the following example:

> If Adam went to the movies, then Betty went also.
> Therefore, if Adam went to the movies, then both Adam and Betty went to the movies.

We can symbolize this argument as:

> A ⊃ B
> Therefore, A ⊃ (A • B).

We could easily prove the validity of this argument by means of a truth table. However, we could not prove it valid by using the Rules of Inference alone. The method of conditional proof in conjunction with the Rules of Inference will enable us to prove its validity.

We can use the method of conditional proof on any argument whose conclusion is a conditional statement. We always begin the method of conditional proof the same way: we <u>assume the antecedent of the conclusion</u> as our first premise. Then we use the Rules of Inference to find the conclusion.

1.	A ⊃ B	Premise
	Therefore, A ⊃ (A • B)	Conclusion
2.	A	Assumed Premise (AP)
3.	B	1, 2, MP
4.	(A • B)	2, 3, Conj.

So far we have proven that if you have an "A" you can get "(A • B)". Therefore, we can assert our conclusion by appealing to line 2 through line 4.

5.	A ⊃ (A • B)	2-4, Conditional Proof (CP)

However, we do not know whether Adam went to the show or not. We just wanted to see what we could conclude <u>if</u> he went to the show. Therefore, we cannot be sure that line 2 ["A"] is true. Nor can we be sure that line 3 ["B"] is true. Nor can we be sure that line 4 ["A • B"] is true. But, nevertheless, we could still validly conclude line 5 ["A ⊃ (A • B)"]. Line 5 does not assert that Adam went to the show or that he did not go to the show. Nor does it assert that the consequent "(A • B)" is the case. It merely asserts that <u>if</u> Adam went to the show, then both Adam and Betty went to the show. Our conclusion is merely a hypothetical statement that does not assert anything factual whatever. So our conclusion does not depend on the truth of lines 2, 3, or 4. It depends only on the original premise [A ⊃ B].

We indicate all this by drawing a black line around the statements whose truth or falsity we do not know. The black line indicates that if the proof were to continue, we could not appeal to the statements enclosed by the black line because we do not know whether they are true or false.

```
1.    A ⊃ B                    Premise
Therefore, A ⊃ (A • B)         Conclusion
2.    A                        Assumed Premise (AP)
3.    B                        1, 2, MP
4.    (A • B)                  2, 3, Conj.
5.    A ⊃ (A • B)              2-4, Conditional Proof (CP)
```

Let's try another example of conditional proof. If the conclusion of an argument contains more than one "if...then" statement, then we may have to use more than one assumed premise. In the following example, the conclusion contains two conditional statements. So we will assume the antecedent of each conditional phrase and end up with two assumed premises. Since we have two assumed premises, we will also need two black lines in order to discharge our two assumptions.

```
1.    (A v B) ⊃ [(C v D) ⊃ E]     Premise
Therefore, A ⊃ [(C • D) ⊃ E]      Conclusion
2.    A                            AP
3.    (A v B)                      2, Add
4.    (C v D) ⊃ E                  1, 3, MP
5.    C • D                        AP
6.    C                            5, Simp
7.    C v D                        6, Add
8.    E                            7, MP
9.    (C • D) ⊃ E                  5-8, CP
10.   A ⊃ [(C • D) ⊃ E]            2-9, CP
```

Indirect Proof

The method of indirect proof is sometimes called *reductio ad absurdum,* which is Latin for "reduction to absurdity". This method tries to <u>disprove</u> an argument by showing the absurd consequences that follow from it. In his geometry, Euclid sometimes begins by assuming the opposite of what he wants to prove. If that assumption leads to a contradiction, then the assumption must be false. So its negation must be true.

In the method of indirect proof, we <u>assume the opposite of what we want to prove</u>. Then we show that the assumption results in a contradiction. This proves the negation of the assumption must be true.

In the following example, we begin by assuming the opposite of what we want to prove, that is, by assuming the negation of our conclusion. Then we show that the assumption results in a contradiction.

1.	A ⊃ B	Premise
2.	B ⊃ C	Premise
3.	A	Premise
Therefore, C		Conclusion
4.	~C	IP (Indirect Proof)
5.	~B	2, 4, MT
6.	~A	1, 5, MT
7.	A • ~A	3, 6, Conj.

There are other ways to prove this conclusion. You could use CA, and MP to get the contradiction (C • ~C). Or you could use MT and MP to get the contradiction (B • ~B).

Now let's put together everything we have learned so far. We will prove the following argument by means of indirect proof.

1.	(x)(Mx ⊃ Px)	Premise
2.	(∃x)(Sx • Mx)	Premise
Therefore, (∃x)(Sx • Px)		Conclusion
3.	~(∃x)(Sx • Px)	IP (Indirect Proof)
4.	Sa • Ma	2, EI
5.	Ma ⊃ Pa	1, UI
6.	(x)~(Sx • Px)	3, QE
7.	~(Sa • Pa)	6, UI
8.	Ma	4, Simp
9.	Pa	5, 8, MP
10.	Sa	4, Simp
11.	Sa • Pa	9, 10, Conj.
12.	(Sa • Pa) • ~(Sa • Pa)	7, 11, Conj.

Remember that you have to use EI before you use UI. Moreover, in this example, you see for the first time why we need QE. Since we cannot instantiate the negation of the existential quantifier, we need QE transform it into a universal quantifier so we can instantiate it. The negation goes through the existential quantifier, the quantifier changes from existential to universal, and the negation comes out the other side of the new quantifier.

In this example, we use not only our Rules of Inference, but also our instantiation and generalization rules, in addition to our rules of conditional and indirect proof. All these rules put together, give us a method of deduction that is complete. Any argument that we can prove valid by a truth table, we can now prove valid by the method of deduction.

The more symbolic logic learns and discovers, the more tasks computers will be able to perform. The following article comes from the December 31, 1990 to January 7, 1991 edition of *U.S. News & World Report*:

FUZZY LOGIC: Computers are getting ever closer to "thinking" like humans. One of the decade's biggest technology challenges will be the effort to free computers from the precise on-off terms of the digital world. Fuzzy-logic circuits accommodate such notions as "many," "about" and "almost," making them useful for automatic cameras' focusing systems, air-conditioner control, automatic transmission and suspension control in cars, and for accelerating and stopping subway trains very smoothly. The first fuzzy-logic products are coming from Japan and include camcorders, washing machines and TV's.

Exercise 21

<u>DIRECTIONS:</u> Prove the following arguments by means of the method of conditional proof.

1. If we go to Asia then we visit China. If we go to Asia, then if we visit China then we see Peking. If we visit China, then if we see Peking then we tour the Forbidden City. Therefore, if we go to Asia then we will tour the Forbidden City. (A, C, P, F)

2. If either Saudi Arabia or Egypt joins the alliance, then if either Lebanon or Jordan boycotts it then although Iran does not boycott it Afghanistan boycotts it. If either Iran or Pakistan does not boycott it then Turkey will join the alliance. Therefore, if Saudi Arabia joins the alliance, then if Lebanon boycotts it then Turkey will join the alliance. (SA, E, L, J, I, A, P, T)

3. Squid and clams are edible mollusks. Therefore, squid is edible.
   (Sx, Cx, Ex, Mx)

4. From the premise "W $\supset$ (X $\supset$ Y)," deduce the conclusion "(~ Y $\bullet$ Z) $\supset$ (X $\supset$ ~ W)."

5. From the premises "J $\supset$ [(K v L) $\supset$ M]" and "(M v N) $\supset$ O," deduce the conclusion "J $\supset$ (L $\supset$ O)."

Exercise 22

Construct a quantificational deduction to show that the argument is logically correct. Use the method of indirect proof.

1. "Something is heavier than something" validly follows from "Everything is heavier than something."

2. If $(\exists x)(y)$ Byx, then $(y)(\exists x)$ Byx.

3. All these rubies are expensive. Whatever disappears will have to be paid for. Therefore, if everything expensive disappears, then all these rubies will have to be paid for. (Rx, Ex, Dx, Px)

Exercise 23

Prove the following argument by the method of conditional proof.

1. 1. J ⊃ K
    2. L ∨ ~J
    ∴   J ⊃ (K • L)

Prove the following argument by the method of indirect proof.

2. 1. Q ∨ R
    2. Q ⊃ R
    ∴   R

Prove the following arguments by the method of conditional proof.

3. 1. (x) (Wx ⊃ Yx)
    ∴   (∃x) Wx ⊃ (∃x) Yx

4. 1. (J ∨ K) ⊃ (L • M)
    2. (M ∨ N) ⊃ O
    ∴   J ⊃ O

Prove the following argument by the method of indirect proof.

5. 1. Q ⊃ T
    2. (R ∨ ~T) ⊃ Q
    ∴   T

Prove the following argument by the method of conditional proof.

6. 1. (x) (Wx ⊃ Zx)
    2. (x) (Wx ⊃ Yx)
    ∴   (x) [Wx ⊃ (Zx • Yx)]

Prove the following arguments by the method of indirect proof.

7. 1. J ⊃ K
    2. L ⊃ J
    3. L ∨ (K • M)
    ∴   K

8. 1. A ∨ B
    2. B ⊃ (C • D)
    3. (C ∨ A) ⊃ E
    ∴   E

Chapter 4
Inductive Logic

Deduction vs. Induction

There is a difference between necessary and empirical sentences. <u>NECESSARY SENTENCES</u> (we are speaking of logical necessity not factual necessity) are sentences whose truth or falsity can be known without evidence from observation. In other words, you can know the truth or falsity of the statement simply by examining the meaning of the words in the sentence. The reason you can do this is that in necessary sentences the idea of the predicate is already contained in the idea of the subject. All necessary sentences are of the form "A is A". For example, "My maternal uncle is my mother's brother". Is this statement true or false? Of course, it is true. You do not have to know anything about my mother to know that it is true. You don't even have to know whether my mother had a brother! You just look at the sentence and you know immediately it is true.

<u>EMPIRICAL SENTENCES</u> are sentences whose truth or falsity depends on evidence from sense experience. In empirical sentences the idea of the predicate is <u>not</u> contained in the idea of the subject. All empirical sentences are of the form "A is B". For example, "My maternal uncle's name is Jean-Paul". Is this statement true or false? You cannot say whether it is true or false. In empirical sentences, you cannot know the truth-value of the statement by simply analyzing the words involved. You have to go out into the world and investigate in order to discover whether the statement is true or false.

There is also a difference between deductive arguments and inductive arguments. A <u>DEDUCTIVE ARGUMENT</u> is an argument whose conclusion follows necessarily from the premises, usually beginning with a general principle and inferring from it a particular fact. Here is an example:

> All men are mortal.
> Socrates is a man.
> Therefore, Socrates is mortal.

Remember that a deductive argument is valid when the conclusion does not go beyond the information contained in the premises.

Let's summarize the important points about deduction:

1. It usually argues from the general to the particular.

2. The conclusion is contained in the premises.

3. A valid deductive argument can result in certainty. If the premises are true and the argument is valid, then the conclusion is necessarily true.

4. This type of reasoning is used primarily in fields like mathematics and geometry.

John Stuart Mill, a 19th century British philosopher, believed that all deductive reasoning contained a fallacy called *petitio principii* (begging the question). *Petitio principii* is a circular argument that begins by assuming the very thing it ends up proving. In his *System of Logic* (book 2, chapter 3), Mill says, "We have now to inquire whether the syllogistic process, that of reasoning from generals to particulars, is or is not a process of inference, a progress from the known to the unknown, a means of coming to a knowledge of something which we did not know before". In other words, Mill is asking if we learn something new from deductive reasoning. Do we discover something that we did not know beforehand when we reason deductively? Mill answers his own question:

> "It is universally allowed that a syllogism is invalid if there be anything more in the conclusion than was assumed in the premises. But this is, in fact, to say that nothing ever was or can be proved by a syllogism which was not known or assumed to be known before." As you well know, a valid deductive argument does not go beyond the information provided by the premises. For example, in the most famous of all syllogisms, the conclusion, "Socrates is mortal", is already contained in the premise "All men are mortal". So the conclusion is merely a restatement of the premise.

Since the conclusion of a valid deductive argument is merely a restatement of the premises, deductive reasoning provides us with no new knowledge. How do we gain new knowledge, then, if not from deduction? Mill continues, "Assuming that the proposition, 'Socrates is mortal,' is immediately an inference from the proposition, 'All men are mortal,' whence do we derive our knowledge of that general truth? Of course, from observation. The true reason why we believe that Socrates will die is that his fathers, and our fathers, and all other persons who were contemporary with them, have died. Those facts are the real premises of the reasoning." We learn new knowledge, not from deduction, but from observation of the world around us. The truth of the premises of a deductive argument is known from our experience of the world. So Mill concludes that the premises of deductive reasoning are based on induction.

An <u>INDUCTIVE ARGUMENT</u> is an argument that claims to yield only probable knowledge, usually beginning with many particular facts and inferring from them a general rule. Here is an example of an inductive argument.

> This swan is white.
> The swans in Central Park are white.
> The swans I saw in Canada last summer were white.
> Therefore, all swans are white.

Is this argument valid? No, it is invalid. Why is it invalid? Because of "insufficient sample". The person who made this argument looked in only three places. Had he looked in more than merely three places, he may well have discovered a black swan. One reason that inductive arguments are only probable is because it would be impossible to examine every single case. Nevertheless, a valid inductive argument must be based on a sufficient sample.

How about a sample size of 2,400,000? That should give you a pretty high level of confidence. Right? During the 1936 presidential campaign, Franklin D. Roosevelt was running against Alf Landon. The *Literary Digest*, a popular American magazine of the time, wanted to know who would win the election. So the magazine sent out 10,000,000 questioners from which they received 2,400,000 responses. On the basis of these responses, the *Literary Digest* predicted that Alf Landon would win the election. Well, what went wrong? They had a gigantic sample, didn't they?

The original sample of 10,000,000 people was selected from telephone listings and automobile registration lists. In 1936, the country was in the depths of the Great Depression so telephones and automobiles were luxuries. Who were the only people who could afford luxuries during the Depression? Rich Republicans! So in this case, the problem was not the size of the sample. The problem was "biased sample".

How do you get a sample that is representative and unbiased? One solution is to take a "random sample", which gives everyone an equal chance to be a member of the sample. Another solution is to create a "representative sample", that is, a small group of people that mirrors the population of the United States as a whole.

Let's enumerate the important points concerning induction:

1. It usually argues from the particular to the general.

2. The conclusion is not wholly contained in the premises.

3. Consequently, the truth of the premises cannot ensure the truth of the conclusion.

4. So induction results in probability statements rather than certainty.

5. This type of reasoning is used primarily in science.

Only deductive arguments give certainty; but their premises are based on induction. This is the tragic problem in being human. The foundation of the only certain knowledge we have is based on mere probability. The tragedy of being human is that we never know what is right until it is too late. Is now the opportune moment to invest in the stock market? Should you accept that recent job offer even though it means uprooting your family and moving to another city? We cannot know the answers to such questions until after the fact. Anyone who has ever bought a used car knows exactly what this means.

This is what Greek tragedy is all about. The tragedy of Oedipus was not due to sin. A sin is something that you know is wrong but do anyway. This was not the case with Oedipus. As soon as he heard the prophecy that he would murder his father and marry his mother, he immediately ran away from home to insure that the prophecy would not come true. The trouble was he did not know that he was adopted. As fate would have it, the town he ran away to was the home of his real parents. Oedipus did, indeed, murder his father and marry his mother. The fate of Oedipus was not due to sin; it was due to ignorance. <u>That</u> is the human predicament! And <u>that</u> is why we are tragic creatures.

I had a physics teacher who said, "If you want to know the truth, do <u>not</u> take a science class." Science can only propose theories. As new facts come to light, these theories are constantly being updated. So it is the very nature of science that it can never result in the truth. My physics teacher said, "If you want to know the truth, take a metaphysics class." Well, I wanted to know the truth! So the next semester, I signed up for a metaphysics class. But I discovered that those philosophers do not know the truth either. All philosophers do is argue with one another. They do not seem to be able to agree on anything!

So now that I am a teacher, I do not even know where to send you, my students, to find the truth. However, I can give you one piece of advice that will make your life much easier if you follow it. Are you ready? Well, here it is: Whenever anyone tells you that they have the truth, the wise thing for you to do is to put both hands around your pocket-book and run as fast as you can in the opposite direction. Because people who claim to have the truth are out to pick your pocket! That especially goes for evangelists, stockbrokers, and politicians!

Many of my students do not like this advice because they came to college to find the truth. They do not appreciate me telling them how difficult it is to find the truth and that it may take them thirty years to do so. Nevertheless, there might be some consolation to the fact that the truth is so difficult to discover.

A number of years ago Jacob Bronowski produced a thirteen-part series on PBS television called *The Ascent of Man*. Bronowski was a Polish Jew who had such a great aptitude for mathematics that he was sent to study in Germany between World War I and World War II. When Hitler came to power, Bronowski escaped to Britain. In the eleventh episode of his series, a program called "Knowledge or Certainty"; he returns to the University of Gottingen and tells how wonderful it was to have had the opportunity to study in Germany between the wars. He tells about all his distinguished teachers, a tale that sounds like a compendium of the great physicists of the early 20th century.

I had a philosophy teacher who used to say that philosophy speaks only two languages: ancient Greek and modern German. No one has been able to match the cultural contributions of the ancient Greeks with the single exception of the Germans. The Germans dominate in science, they dominate in music, and they dominate in philosophy.

Toward the end of the eleventh episode, Bronowski visits Auschwitz, a concentration camp in Poland, where most of his family was gassed to death. In this episode he is grappling with a single question: How could the Germans, who contributed so much to Western civilization, have become such barbarians? His answer? They thought they had the truth! Bronowski thinks that whenever human beings think they have the truth, they become barbarians. When the Romans thought that they had the truth, they behaved barbarically toward the Christians. When the Christians thought that they had the truth, they behaved barbarically with their crusades and inquisitions.

We can apply this principle not only to nations but also to ourselves personally. If you think that you have the truth, you are going to behave barbarically toward your younger brothers and sisters. If you are a parent and you think you have the truth, you are going to behave barbarically toward your children. If you are a teacher and you think you have the truth, you are going to behave barbarically toward your students. So perhaps the realization that it is almost impossible to know the truth might prevent us from acting barbarically, especially toward those people who we love the most.

How are deductive and inductive arguments alike? Remember we said earlier that deductive reasoning might reach a true conclusion even though it is not a valid, logical argument? In other words, we have examples of deductive reasoning whose conclusion is true but whose argument is, nevertheless, invalid. The same thing can happen with inductive reasoning. The conclusion of an inductive argument may be true even though the argument is invalid. Here is an example. Let's say that it is raining. You will inevitably hear someone say, "I knew it was going to rain today because I washed my car yesterday!"

How are deductive and inductive arguments different? We said earlier that if a deductive argument contains true premises and is logically sound, then its conclusion will necessarily be true. This is not the case with inductive arguments. An inductive argument may contain true premises and be a logically sound argument, but still have a false conclusion. A good example is the weatherman. His premises are very scientific: he sends up balloons to get an accurate radar picture, he studies the winds and other atmospheric conditions. On the basis of these true premises, he makes his predictions, which often turn out to be wrong. His arguments are sound but his conclusion is often false.

What is the difference between deductive and inductive validity? To find the answer to this question, first consider another question: What was our criterion for validity of deductive arguments? What does validity mean in deductive arguments? Well, we said that a deductive argument is valid if its conclusion follows logically from its premises. However, the criterion of validity must be different for inductive arguments because an inductive conclusion expresses conjectures that go beyond the premises. So what is the criterion for inductive validity?

An inductive argument is valid if the degree of probability claimed by its conclusion is reasonable in relation to its premises. In other words, validity requires that the conclusion must assert the same degree of probability that the premises indicate.

If an event is impossible, it has a probability of 0 (zero). If an event is certain to occur, it has a probability of 1 (one). So all of the other probabilities are between 0 and 1.

If the weatherman says there is an 80% chance of rain tomorrow, it means there are eight chances out of ten that it will rain. What's the probability that you will wake up tomorrow morning? Some students tell me that the probability is fifty/fifty. I often wonder what type of activity these students plan to indulge in after class. Let's say you are on an operating table and you ask the surgeon, "Doc, what are my chances of survival?" If he answers, "Fifty/fifty", I doubt that you would take much consolation from such a prognosis. The chances of <u>my</u> waking up tomorrow morning are much better than fifty/fifty. I would say that they are in the vicinity of .99 because after class I go home, have dinner, read or watch TV a little, and then go to bed. Probably the same is true of you. That means there are 99 chances out of 100 that you will wake up tomorrow morning. But that does not mean that it is true that you will wake up tomorrow because that one chance out of 100 may come tonight. So when is the last time you checked your smoke alarms?

Since we have already discussed Mill's criticism of deduction, it seems only fair to consider Hume's criticism of induction. If deduction is susceptible to the *petitio principii* fallacy, then induction is susceptible to the *post hoc ergo propter hoc* fallacy. *Post hoc ergo propter hoc* means, "After this, therefore, because of this". The fallacy says that just because event "A" preceded event "B", does not necessarily mean that event "A" caused event "B". You hear this fallacy every time it rains. Someone inevitably says, "I knew it was going to rain today because I washed my car yesterday".

Hume does not reject induction. He's merely saying: Be careful when you reason inductively! If the guy who washed his car had kept track of what happened the next day every time he washed the car, he would have discovered that there is no connection between washing his car and rain the next day. Hume thinks that causal arguments are legitimate if and only if, you have observed the constant conjunction of the two events many, many times.

Hume uses his criticism of induction to disprove the cosmological argument for the existence of God. The cosmological argument is any argument that begins with the world around us and asserts that the world requires a sufficient cause for its existence. The problem with the cosmological argument is that we cannot observe the constant conjunction of cause and effect in the case of God's creation. The only thing we observe is God's creative effect. We never observe it conjoined with the cause because the creation was a singular event. Since we cannot observe constant conjunction of these two events, the cosmological argument leaves us wide open to the *post hoc ergo propter hoc* fallacy.

How can you distinguish deductive from inductive arguments? There are at least three ways:

1. Does the argument go from the general to the particular or from the particular to the general? If it argues from the general to the particular, it is deductive. If it argues from the particular to the general, it is inductive.

2. Is the conclusion certain or merely probable? If the conclusion is certain, it is deductive. If the conclusion is probable, it is inductive.

3. Is the conclusion contained in the premises or does the conclusion go beyond the premises? If the conclusion is contained in the premises, the argument is deductive. If the conclusion goes beyond the premises, the argument is inductive.

Exercise 24

DIRECTIONS: Specify the premises and conclusions of the following arguments and determine whether they are deductive or inductive. State the reason why you believe the arguments to be deductive or inductive.

1. The three angles of a triangle are equal to 180 degrees. Therefore, the angles of the triangle hanging on the Christmas tree are equal to two right angles.
2. There must be life on Venus because there are so many parallels between Earth and Venus.
3. Nature has its own solution to the two-headed monster of overpopulation, on the one hand, and limited natural resources on the other. Nature's solution is the four horsemen of the Apocalypse: Famine, Plague, War, and Death. Therefore, if we do not limit our own population ourselves, nature will solve the problem for us.
4. "...I've always reckoned that looking at the new moon over your left shoulder is one of the most careless and foolish things a body can do. Old Hank Bunker done it once, and bragged about it; and in less than two years he got drunk and fell off the shot tower, and spread himself out so that he was just a kind of a layer, as you may say; and they slid him edgeways between two barn doors for a coffin, and buried him so, so they say, but I didn't see it. Pap told me. But anyway it all came of looking at the moon that way, like a fool."
5. Ricky is the cousin of Lance. Lance is the cousin of Michael. Therefore, Ricky is the cousin of Michael.
6. I think that the method of induction has been pretty much discredited. Induction considers many particular facts and draws from them a universal law. If you merely take a sampling of the facts, the induction will be tenuous at best. Moreover, it is impossible to consider all of the facts since everything is always changing and evolving. So induction, by its very nature, must be tenuous and incomplete. Therefore, we can banish the method of induction altogether.
7. Julius and Ethel Rosenberg were executed in 1953 for passing information about the atomic bomb to the Soviet Union. The Verona Project seems to indicate that at least Julius was guilty of espionage. But critics doubt that he was guilty of the charges brought against him. So Julius may have been innocent.
8. [In his letters to Louise Colet, Flaubert] boasts of amorous exploits, which must be true, since he is addressing the only person who can be both witness and judge of them. (Jean-Paul Sartre, Search for a Method)
9. We made our initial observations on the black Austrian honeybee... An extremely simple experiment suffices to demonstrate that these insects do communicate. If one puts a small dish of sugar water near a beehive, the dish may not be discovered for several days. But as soon as one bee has found the dish and returned to the hive, more foragers come from the same hive. In an hour hundreds may be there. (Karl Von Frisch, "Dialects in the Language of the Bees," Scientific American, p. 79, August, 1962.)
10. No, do not ring the doorbell because you will wake him up. The drapes are closed so he must still be sleeping.

11. ...the class of all classes that have more than five members clearly has more than five classes as members; therefore, the class is a member of itself. On the other hand, the class of all men is not a member of itself, not being a man. What of the class of all classes that are not members of themselves? Since its members are the nonself-members, it qualifies as a member of itself if and only if it is not. It is and is not a member of itself. (W. V. O. Quine, "Paradox," Scientific American, p. 84, April, 1962.)

12. "Hondas are well made, reliable, and gas efficient. All the more reason why you should make you next car a Honda.

13. Carlos loves Brittany. Brittany loves Ricky.
    Therefore, Carlos loves Ricky.

14. "But I don't want to go among mad people," Alice remarked.
    "Oh, you can't help that," said the Cat: "We're all mad here. I'm mad. You're mad."
    "How do you know I'm mad?" said Alice.
    "You must be," said the Cat, "or you wouldn't have come here."
    (Lewis Carroll, Alice in Wonderland.)

Exercise 25

DIRECTIONS: Are the following sentences necessarily true, necessarily false, or empirical?

1. It will either rain or it won't rain.

2. It will either rain or snow

3. All limousines are black.

4. All limousines are luxurious.

5. No atheists believe in God.

6. All deists believe in a providential, caring God.

7. You are either for me on this issue or you are not!

8. You are either for me or against me.

9. Not all cats are feline.

10. All Americans are patriotic.

11. John Mitchell: "When the going gets tough, the tough get going."

   (During the Watergate affair, when John Dean [President Nixon's attorney] told John Mitchell [the Attorney General] that there was a cancer growing on the presidency, John Dean testified that John Mitchell made this comment.)

Exercise 26

<u>DIRECTIONS</u>: For each of the following arguments, identify the conclusion, state whether you think the argument is deductive or inductive, and give a reason for you answer.

1. Mark and Betty are always together. I saw Betty here at the party tonight. So Mark must be here too.

2. Experience confirms that whenever it rains in California, it pours. Since it is starting to rain this morning, it is likely to pour later on this afternoon.

3. Whenever interest rates go up, the value of your bonds goes down. So since interest rates are rising, prepare to lose money on your bonds.

4. Los Angeles has a larger population than San Francisco, and San Francisco has a larger population than Santa Barbara. So Los Angeles must have a larger population than Santa Barbara.

5. It snows in San Francisco every ten years. Since it has been ten years since it last snowed, you can bet that it will snow this winter.

6. The American Cancer Society advises us to eat lots of colorful fruits and vegetables. The color contains anti-oxidants, which help to prevent cancer.

7. Every Italian I have ever met has been Catholic. So all Italians must be Catholic.

8. All rationalists are believers in the power of reason. No Empiricists are rationalists. So no Empiricists are believers in the power of reason.

9. Whenever Betty goes to Mexico, she always buys jewelry. Betty went to Mexico last month, so she must have bought some jewelry.

10. John Smith, a well-know economist at a local university, says that we will have another stock-market crash due to the fact that we never fixed what caused the last stock-market crash, namely, lack of regulation for the Wall-Street big-wigs and underemployment for the rest of us.

Probability Theory

Probability is the "chances" or "likelihood" that an event will take place. Probability equals the expected frequency divided by the total frequency. If an event is certain to occur, it has a probability of 1. If an event is impossible, it has a probability of 0.

Law of Negation

The probability of a particular event <u>not</u> taking place equals one (1) minus the probability that the event does take place. We can summarize this definition of the Law of Negation by the following formula:

$$\sim P(A) = 1 - P(A)$$

This formula says that the probability of event A not occurring equals one minus the probability that event A does occur. Let's consider the following example. Answer the question by using the formula for the Law of Negation. What is the probability of not rolling a six on the next roll of a die? (A die has six sides numbered from one through six.)

$$
\begin{aligned}
\sim P(A) \;\; &= 1 - P(A) \\
&= 1 - 1/6 \\
&= 5/6
\end{aligned}
$$

Law of Conjunction

There are two formulas for the Law of Conjunction depending on whether we are considering "independent events" or "dependent events".

<u>INDEPENDENT EVENTS</u> is a situation in which the occurrence of one event does not affect the probability of the occurrence of the other event. For example, the fact that you have had four girls in a row does not increase the probability that your next child will be a boy. Each birth is completely independent of the previous births as far as the sex of the newborn child is concerned. To find the probability of two independent events happening, multiply the individual probabilities. We can summarize the Law of Conjunction for independent events "A" and "B" by the following formula:

$$P(A \bullet B) = P(A) \times P(B)$$

This formula says that the probability of event A and event B both occurring equals the probability that event A occurs times the probability that event B occurs. Let's consider the following example. Answer the question using the formula of Law of Conjunction for independent events. What is the probability of getting heads on the first and the second toss of a coin?

$$P(A \bullet B) = P(A) \times P(B)$$
$$= 1/2 \times 1/2$$
$$= 1/4$$

DEPENDENT EVENTS is a situation in which the occurrence of one event changes the probability of the occurrence of the second event. To find the probability of two dependent events happening, multiply the probability of the first event by the probability of the second event, assuming that the first event is true. We can summarize the Law of Conjunction for dependent events by the following formula:

$$P(A \bullet B) = P(A) \times P(B/A)$$

This formula says that the probability of both events A and B occurring equals the probability that event A occurs times the probability that event B occurs, given the fact that event A occurs. Try to solve the following example by using the above formula of the Law of Conjunction for dependent events. A bag contains 3 yellow and 4 blue balls. Let 2 balls be withdrawn in succession without replacing the first ball. What is the probability that the first ball is yellow and the second is blue?

$$P(A \bullet B) = P(A) \times P(B/A)$$
$$= 3/7 \times 4/6$$
$$= 12/42$$
$$= 6/21$$
$$= 2/7$$

Law of Disjunction

There are also two formulas for the Law of Disjunction depending on whether we are talking about "non-mutually exclusive events" or "mutually exclusive events".

NON-MUTUALLY EXCLUSIVE EVENTS is a situation in which it is possible for both events to occur simultaneously. The Law of Disjunction for non-mutually exclusive events says that the probability of one event or another event happening is equal to the sum of their separate probabilities minus the probability of their conjunction. We can summarize the probability of event A or event B happening by the following formula:

$$P(A \lor B) = P(A) + P(B) - P(A \bullet B)$$

This formula says that the probability of event A or event B happening equals the probability that event A occurs plus the probability that event B occurs minus the probability that both event A and event B occurs. Try to figure out the following example by using the above formula of the Law of Disjunction for non-mutually exclusive events. What is the probability of getting either a red card or a queen when drawing a card from an ordinary deck of playing cards? (There are 52 cards in a deck, half are red and half are black. There are 4 suits in a deck: hearts, diamonds, clubs, and spades. Each suit has 13 cards from ace through king.)

$$P(A \lor B) = P(A) + P(B) - P(A \bullet B)$$
$$= 26/52 + 4/52 - 2/52$$
$$= 28/52$$
$$= 14/26$$
$$= 7/13$$

Look at the very last part of the Law of Disjunction for non-mutually exclusive events: $P(A \bullet B)$. What does it remind you of? Of course, it is the Law of Conjunction. The example I have given is so simple that you can do it in your head. But things will not always be this simple! So you have to learn how to expand the very last part of the formula by the Law of Conjunction. The first question you have to ask yourself when doing the Law of Conjunction is: Are we dealing with independent events or dependent events? Try to answer this question using our example with the playing cards before you look at the next sentence. No fair peeking! If you answered independent events, you are right. Now here is the more important question: Why did you say independent events? Try to answer the question before you look at the next sentence. The answer is: because we are drawing only one card.

Now you are ready to write down the formula to figure the probability. The formula for Law of Conjunction, independent events is:

$$P(A \bullet B) = P(A) \times P(B)$$
$$= 26/52 \times 4/52$$
$$= 2/52$$

MUTUALLY EXCLUSIVE EVENTS is a situation in which the occurrence of one event excludes the occurrence of the other event. In other words, it is a situation where both events cannot occur. The Law of Disjunction says that to find the probability of mutually exclusive events, we add the individual probabilities. We can summarize the probability of event "A" or event "B" happening by the following formula:

$$P(A \lor B) = P(A) + P(B)$$

Use the formula to figure out the answer to the following example. Suppose a die is thrown. What is the probability that it will fall either a 2 or a 6.

$$P(A \lor B) = P(A) + P(B)$$
$$= 1/6 + 1/6$$
$$= 1/3$$

That's all there is too it. Here is the best way to solve probability problems:

1. Ask yourself if this is an "and" question or an "or" question. Is the problem asking for the probability that event "A" <u>and</u> event "B" takes place? Or is the problem asking for the probability that event "A" <u>or</u> event "B" takes place? If the problem is asking for the probability that event "A" <u>and</u> event "B" occurs, use the Law of Conjunction. If the problem is asking for the probability that event "A" <u>or</u> event "B" occurs, use the Law of Disjunction.

2. If you are using the Law of Conjunction, ask yourself whether the events are dependent or independent. If you are using the Law of Disjunction, ask yourself whether the events are mutually exclusive or not. Then write down the formula and follow it exactly. (If you follow these suggestions, you will have no problem with probability. DO NOT THINK, just follow the rules!)

Test yourself on the following example:

"Three cards are drawn in succession with no replacement from a pack of 52. What is the probability that all three are aces?"

I am not so interested in your doing the math in this problem. The real challenge here is that you must transform the formula to handle three events, event "A", event "B", and event "C". The formulas I have given you cover only two events, event "A" and event "B". So I want you to create a new formula based on the ones I have given you. Expand the correct formula to three places and write in the probabilities for all three events. Do not worry so much about the math.

You can find the answer to this question at the end of this section.

Here is another example that allows you to test yourself.

"A player at draw poker holds the 7 of clubs and the 8, 9, 10 and ace of hearts. He could try for a straight or a flush. What should he do?"

(A straight is five cards in numerical sequence, any suit. A flush is five cards all of the same suit, any sequence. Do not worry about what cards the other players have. When you play poker, you do not know that information.)

DIRECTIONS: Calculate the probability of a straight by using the probability rules; calculate the probability of a flush in your head. (You can find the answers to these two questions at the end of this section.)

What do we mean by the word "or" in logic? We do not mean "this or that" in an exclusive sense; we mean "either this or that or perhaps both."

If you were asked, "What is the probability of getting 6 at least once in two throws of a die?" You would use this formula: $P(A \vee B) = P(A) + P(B) - P(A \bullet B)$. You win if it comes up a 6 on the first toss, you win if it comes up 6 on the second toss, and you win if it comes up 6 on both tosses. If you win when you get a 6 on both tosses, then why do we subtract the final part of the formula: $P(A \bullet B)$? I do not want you to try to answer this question because I am about to answer it myself. I just want you to see the problem!

Here is the answer. Let's say that I have two overlapping circles. Both circles are made of a felt material. The left circle "A" represents the probability of getting a 6 on the first toss. The right circle "B" represents the probability of getting a 6 on the second toss.

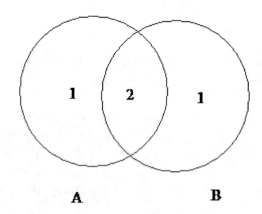

I win if it comes up "A"; I win if it comes up "B". And I win if it comes up "A" and "B" (the overlapping area). Please remember that these are felt circles. Therefore, the crescent shape on the left and the crescent shape on the right have a thickness of one. However, where the circles overlap in the middle (the football-shaped area), there is a thickness of 2. That is why we have to subtract $P(A \bullet B)$. We are counting it twice due to the overlap, whereas we should count it only once.

Now consider this problem: "What is the probability of getting heads at least once in three tosses of a coin?" Remember how we earlier had to expand the Law of Conjunction so that we could consider three events? Well, now we have to expand the Law of Disjunction to consider three events. This is not as easy as expanding the Law of Conjunction so I am not going to ask you to try to do it yourself. Instead, I am going to give you the formula. But first you have to tell me if we are dealing with non-mutually exclusive events or mutually exclusive events. Answer this question before you look at the next sentence. If you answered non-mutually exclusive, you are correct. Now tell me why is it non-mutually exclusive before looking at the next sentence. Because we could get heads on all three tosses. Here is our original formula for Law of Disjunction non-mutually exclusive events:

$$P(A \vee B) = P(A) + P(B) - P(A \bullet B)$$

Here is the same formula but now expanded for three events. It is rather long so I may not be able to get all of it on one line:

$$P(A \vee B \vee C) = P(A) + P(B) + P(C) - P(A \bullet B) - P(A \bullet C)$$
$$- P(B \bullet C) + P(A \bullet B \bullet C).$$

There it is! Now, of course, you know why we have to subtract the P(A • B) and the P(A • C) and the P(B • C). We have to get the overlaps out so we do not count them twice. But why on earth do we add the P(A • B • C)?

Are you still thinking about the felt circles? If we had three partially overlapping felt circles, we would have the following thickness of felt layers for the various sets:

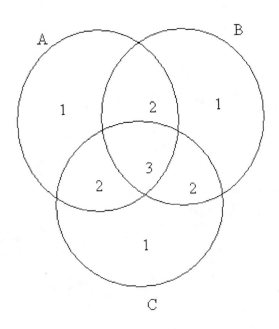

When we subtract P(A • B), we end up with the following layers of thickness:

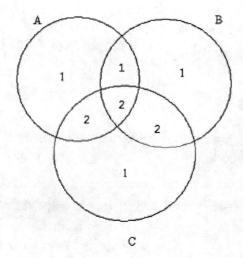

When we subtract P(A • C), we end up with the following layers of thickness:

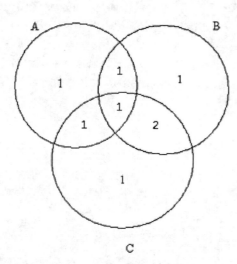

When we subtract P(B • C), we end up with the following layers of thickness:

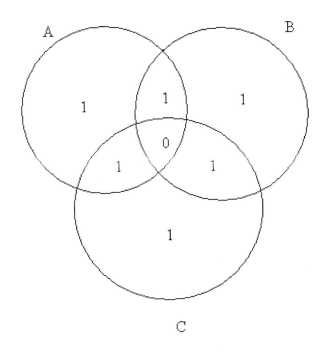

That is why we have to add in the P(A • B • C).

Work the problem to find the probability of heads at least once in three tosses. (What question do you have to ask yourself when expanding the Law of Conjunction?)

Find the solution to this problem at the end of this section.

<u>Answers</u>:
Law of Conjunction, dependent events expanded for 3 events:

$$P(A • B • C) = P(A) \times P(B/A) \times P(C/A • B)$$
$$= 4/52 \times 3/51 \times 2/50$$
$$= 24/132,600$$
$$= 1/5525$$
$$= .0001809$$

The probability of a straight: He holds a 7, 8, 9, and 10. So he needs a 6 or a jack in order to get a straight.

Is this an "and" or an "or" question? He needs a 6 or a jack. So we use the Law of Disjunction.

Are we dealing with non-mutually exclusive events or mutually exclusive events? He is going to give the dealer only one card, the ace. So he is going to get back only one card from the dealer. It is impossible for him to get both a 6 and a jack. So the events are mutually exclusive.

Law of Disjunction, mutually exclusive events:

$$P(A \lor B) = P(A) + P(B)$$
$$= 4/47 + 4/47$$
$$\mathbf{= 8/47}$$

The probability of a flush: He holds the 8, 9, 10, and ace of hearts. He needs one more heart to get the flush. There are 13 hearts in the deck. He has four of them. Thirteen minus 4 equals 9. There are 9 hearts left. The probability of getting the flush is:

9/47

What should he do? It is a little more likely that he will get the flush.

$$
\begin{aligned}
P(A \lor B \lor C) &= P(A)+P(B)+P(C)-P(A \cdot B)-P(A \cdot C)-P(B \cdot C)+P(A \cdot B \cdot C). \\
&= 1/2 + 1/2 + 1/2 - (1/2 \bullet 1/2) - (1/2 \bullet 1/2) - (1/2 \bullet 1/2) + (1/2 \bullet 1/2 \bullet 1/2) \\
&= \quad 1\ 1/2 - 1/4 \quad - 1/4 \quad - 1/4 \quad + 1/8 \\
&= \quad 12/8 - 6/8 \quad + 1/8 \\
&= 7/8
\end{aligned}
$$

Exercise 27

DIRECTIONS: Decide which probability law applies, write the law on a piece of paper, then add the numerical probabilities in order to answer the question.

1. Let's say you are playing with a standard deck of 52 playing cards. You withdraw one card and then return it to the deck. Then you withdraw a second card. What is the probability that both cards are clubs?
2. What is the probability that at least one of the two cards you withdrew in Question 1 is a club?
3. Now let's say you withdraw one card but you do not return it to the deck. Then you withdraw a second card. What is the probability that both cards are diamonds?
4. What is the probability that at least one of the two cards you withdrew in Question 3 is a diamond?
5. Suppose you withdraw three cards and do not return any of them to the deck. What is the probability that at least one is a diamond?
6. What is the probability that all three cards in Question 5 are diamonds?
7. Limp Biscuit is running in today's race at Santa Anita. The bookmakers have set the odds of his winning at 1 to 3. The odds are even that he will win at Hollywood Park next week if he wins today at Santa Anita. What is the probability that he wins both races? (To convert odds to probability: add both numbers together and make the sum the denominator of the probability. To convert probability to odds: subtract the numerator from the denominator.)
8. If Limp Biscuit wins both races at Santa Anita and Hollywood Park, then the odds of his winning at Bay Meadows next month is 3 to 2. What is the probability that he wins all three races? What odds would the bookmaker give him to win all three races?
9. On earth the population is divided equally between two sexes: male and female. However, on Venus the population is divided equally among three sexes: pi, rho, and sigma. Is it more likely that an earth couple who are going to have two children will have at least one female child or that a Venusian triple who are going to have three children will have at least one sigma child?

Chapter 5
Informal Logic

Informal Fallacies

Argument Against the Person

Latin name: *argumentum ad hominem* (argument directed to the man).

There are two forms of this argument:

1. **Abusive Argument** – an attack on the person rather than his argument.

Examples:

During election campaigns, you often hear this fallacy, otherwise known as mudslinging: Vice President Agnew referred to journalists who criticized the Nixon administration as "an impudent corps of effete snobs."

Father to son: "Let's examine the credentials of your new friend. First, he has an unruly beard. Second, he has never shown any initiative in getting a job and supporting himself. Third, he uses drugs. And now he says that our foreign policy is bankrupt! How can you expect me to take that statement seriously?"

2. **Circumstantial Argument** – cites the opponent's personal circumstances as sufficient reason for dismissing his argument.

Examples:

During a debate on welfare costs, a woman stands up and says: "I think that welfare benefits should be increased because the present rate makes it impossible to feed, house, clothe, and educate your children." Then a man stands up and says: "Well, of course, she thinks welfare benefits should be raised because she's on welfare."

When the Ventura County Community College District Board of Trustees was considering holding some of its meetings at night, one of my students addressed the Board, saying that she would appreciate an occasional evening meeting because she had to work during the day and consequently could only attend at night. A member of the Board asked her if she was an employee of the college because the Board was primarily interested in the view of the general public rather than the view of employees. She told him that she was an employee of the college (she was secretary to the dean of counseling) but added, "I have been a life-long resident of Ventura County and I'm very interested in everything that happens in the county." This illustrious member of the Board replied, "Oh, but you are much too young to be a life-long resident!"

Appeal to Force – an attempt to persuade by fear and intimidation.

Latin name: *argumentum ad baculum* (appeal to the stick).

Examples:

If you have ever gone to church, you may have heard this fallacy during the pastor's sermon.

Are you a parent? If so, I hope you have <u>never</u> used this fallacy in an attempt to get your children to clean up their room!

College President: "This college does not need a teacher's union, and any member of the faculty who thinks it does will discover his error at the next tenure review."

Appeal to Authority – an attempt to persuade by appealing to the prestige of a person who is not an authority on the subject under consideration.

Latin name: *argumentum ad verecundiam* (argument toward reverence).

Examples:

"The world of science contains many examples of great men and women who believed in God, so God must exist."

Advertisement: "Brad Pitt drinks only Seagrams!"

Appeal to Pity – an attempt to persuade by arousing sympathy.

Latin name: *argumentum ad misericordiam.*

Examples:

Teachers hear this one a lot: "My dog ate it!"

Newspaper report: "A youth was tried for the horrible crime of murdering his mother and father with a butcher knife. He begged the court for leniency on the grounds that he was an orphan."

Appeal to the Public – an attempt to persuade by manipulating the passions and prejudices of a specific audience.

Latin name: *argumentum ad populum* (appeal to the people or to the gallery).

Examples:

There is a famous example from a play by Shakespeare. It is part of a speech that is extremely well known. You probably had to memorize it in high school. The first line is often quoted.

Find the answer at the end of this section.

"Seventy percent of American women use Ajax Cleanser!"

Argument From Ignorance – an argument that maintains that a proposition is true simply because it has not been proved false, or false because it has not been proved true.

Latin name: *argumentum ad ignorantiam.*

This argument is fallacious because the burden of proof always falls on the person who advances the thesis, not on the person who opposes it.

Examples:

"There is simply no evidence whatever for the existence of intelligent life on another planet. Therefore, we must conclude that intelligent beings exist only on earth."

"Telepathic claims are false because their truth has not been established."

"There is no Loch Ness monster because no one has ever been able to prove it."

Accident – fallacy of applying a general rule to a particular case to which the rule was not intended to apply.

Examples:

"New cars run better than old ones. So my Volkswagen ought to run better than your twenty year old Rolls Royce"

"This medicine works for horses!"

False Cause – an argument that claims that merely because one event precedes another event, the first is the cause of the second.

Latin name: *post hoc ergo propter hoc* (after this, therefore because of this).

Examples:

"Uncle Louie says he has lived to celebrate his hundredth birthday because all his life he ate garlic and drank a shot of whiskey every day."

"I knew it would rain today because I washed my car yesterday".

Two rats are in a Skinner box. One rat says to the other: "Boy, have I got this experimenter conditioned! Every time I press the bar, he gives me a pellet of food." (From a cartoon by Jester of Columbia University)

Irrelevant Conclusion – any *non sequitur*: no connection between the premise and the conclusion.

Latin name: *ignoratio elenchi* (ignorance of the proof).

Use this one sparingly because all informal fallacies are fallacious because their conclusion is irrelevant.

Examples:

Two wealthy businessmen are having a drink at their exclusive club. One says to the other: "If God had not wanted an oil depletion allowance, why would He have created an oil lobby?"

"Crime is so rampant in California that we need a *three-strikes-and-you're-out* law".

Black and white fallacy or False Dilemma – consists of presenting an argument as if there were fewer possible solutions to the problem than is actually the case.

Examples:

"America – love it or leave it!"

"Better dead than red!"

"My county right or wrong!"

"Congressman Izzy Graft agrees that politicians shouldn't go around the country saying dumb things, but he declares there are no other effective ways of getting attention these days."

Hasty Generalization – an argument whose conclusion is based on observations of a sample that is unrepresentative or too small.

Examples:

"President Kennedy died in office because ever since the time of William Henry Harrison, every man who was elected to the presidency in a year with a number that ended in zero has died while in office." (This curiosity is called the "Curse of Tecumseh". After being defeated by Harrison at the Battle of Tippecanoe, Indian Chief Tecumseh put this curse on the presidency.)

"I had a bad time with my former husband. From that experience I've learned that all men are go good."

"I know one union representative and he's a terrible person. I wouldn't trust any of them."

Begging the Question – a circular argument that begins by assuming the very thing it attempts to prove.

Latin name: *petitio principii* (postulation of the beginning).

Examples:

Dr. Hackenbush applies for a loan:
> LOAN OFFICER: How can our bank be sure that you will repay this loan, Dr. Hackenbush?
> HACKENBUSH: Well, I think Mr. Marx will give me a good recommendation.
> LOAN OFFICER: Wonderful! But can the bank trust Mr. Marx?
> HACKENBUSH: Indeed it can, sir! I vouch for the word of Mr. Marx myself!

"God exists because the Bible tells us so, and we know that the Bible is true because it is the revealed word of God."

Archie Bunker: "Seventy-five percent of all needless operations are totally unnecessary".

Live from the Super Bowl during an interview with a Viking player:
> ANNOUNCER: "What, in your opinion, will determine the outcome of this game?"
> VIKING PLAYER: "The final score will determine the outcome."

Two Wrongs Make a Right – an attempt to absolve one's self from wrong doing by claiming that others do things just as bad.

Latin name: *tu quoque* (you, too).

Examples:

Can you think of an example you might hear around income tax time?

If any of you are parents, have you ever heard your kids using one of these?
     SIX-YEAR-OLD: "He hit me first."
     TEENAGER: "But, Mom, all the other kids are doing it."

A little old lady is selling pornographic magazines on a street corner. When an old friend of hers happens by, the little old lady tries to defend herself by saying, "What's obscene to me, Mable, is my son wanting to stick me away in a retirement home!"

Division – arguing that what is true of a whole must also be true of its parts.

Examples:

"This is the best hospital in the whole state; therefore, all the surgeons here are excellent."

"Kent must be wealthy because he is a member of one of the richest fraternities on campus."

Composition – arguing that what is true of the parts must also be true of the whole.

Examples:

"The all-star team is composed of the best players in the league, therefore, it must be the best team."

"Each scene of the play was done so excellently that I am sure that the whole play will be excellent."

Complex Question – framing a question in such a way, that no matter how you answer it, you get in trouble.

Examples:

"Have you stopped beating your wife yet?"

You and your wife go out for dinner. She points out someone and asks you: "Honey, do you think that girl is attractive?"

You come home late one night from a date. Your mother is waiting up for you and asks: "Did you have a good time, dear?"

You nervously go into your boss's office. He is sitting behind a huge desk, looks over at you and asks, "I don't like yes-men, Alex – do you agree?" (Adapted from the cartoon "Frank & Ernest" by Thaves)

Accent – a fallacy in which the meaning of the sentence is ambiguous due to what parts of it may be <u>emphasized</u>.

Examples:

A congressman's secretary tells her boss, "I think you are over-reacting, Congressman. Just because a voter phones and tells you he hopes you get what you deserve is not a threat on your life."

A guy and a girl are in bed. She says to him, "I'll say this about you, Harry, a little bit goes a long way!"

Amphiboly – a fallacy in which the meaning of the sentence is ambiguous due to its <u>grammatical</u> <u>construction</u>.

Examples:

You return home from school and your mother tells you: "We are having Aunt Martha for dinner."

Tommy Ptomaine's Cookbook suggests that you serve oysters when thoroughly stewed.

During World War II, there were a lot of propaganda sayings like "Loose lips sink ships." One poster read: "Save Soap and Waste Paper".

Sign at a roadside restaurant and service station: "Eat here and gas up".

Announcement in a newspaper: "The marriage of Miss Beverly Merrill and Mr. Peter Lynch, which was announced in this newspaper a few weeks ago, was a mistake and we wish to correct it."

Equivocation – uses the same word in different senses in the same context. That is, the word changes meaning in the same argument. (Do not get equivocation mixed up with amphiboly.)

Examples:

"We want a responsible man for this job," said the employer to the applicant. "Well," said the young fellow, "I guess I'm your man. No matter where I've worked, whenever anything happened, they always said I was responsible." (Management Digest)

The customs agent poked through an old gentleman's luggage and found a bottle of wine. "I thought you said there was nothing in here but clothing," he said. "That's true," said the old gent. "That there's my nightcap!" (Lucille Harper)

A person who was building a garage needed some two-by-fours so he went to the lumber yard. The lumberman asked him, "Well, how long do you need them?" The customer replied, "For a long time, I'm building a garage!"

A nurse is pushing a patient in a wheelchair down a hospital corridor. She says to him, "Your doctor has suggested shock treatment, so I'm taking you to the business office to look at you bill".

A guy's house is on fire so he frantically calls the fire department: "What do you mean, 'How do you get here?' Don't you have those big red fire trucks anymore?" (From the cartoon "Bumper Snickers" by Bill Hoest)

How to Identify Informal Fallacies

Construct a chart like the one that follows. Since you will always be asked to choose the best fallacy, go through the whole list before you make your final choice. Some examples may have more than one possibility, but you will always be asked to identify the **best one**.

Informal Fallacies

Against the Person (ad hominem)
  1) abusive
  2) circumstantial

Appeal to force (ad baculum)

Appeal to Authority (ad verecundiam)

Appeal to Pity   (ad misericordiam)

Appeal to the Public (ad populum)

Argument from Ignorance – it's T because it hasn't been proved F.

Accident – applying a rule where it doesn't fit.

False Cause – because event A preceded event B, A caused B.

Irrelevant Conclusion – no connection between premise and conclusion.

False Dilemma (Black and white fallacy) – saying there are fewer solution than is the case.

Hasty Generalization – based on small or unrepresentative sample.

Begging the Question – circular argument.

Tu quoque Fallacy (Two Wrongs make a Right)

Division – what is T of whole is T of parts.

Composition – what is T of parts is T of whole.

Complex Question

Accent – meaning shifts due to emphasis.

Amphiboly – meaning shifts due to grammatical construction.

Equivocation – using same word in different senses.

Answer:
Mark Antony's speech from *Julius Caesar*: "Friends, Romans, and Countrymen, lend me your ears".

Exercise 28

<u>DIRECTIONS</u>: Do any of the following arguments contain informal fallacies? If so, name the fallacy.

Appeal to pity 1. You cannot flunk me, professor, it would break my mother's heart!

Against the Person Abusive 2. Frank Layden, Utah Jazz coach, on Denver Nugget Coach Doug Moe: "I understand Doug gave his wife a water bed. She called it the Dead Sea." – Reader's Digest

Composition 3. Mark is a nice boy and Betty is a nice girl. I am sure they would make a wonderful couple.

Amphiboly 4. I returned home from a nearby farm with two large buckets of cow manure for our garden. "What's that for?" my six-year-old asked. "The strawberries," I answered. After staring at the manure for a minute, he asked, "Can I have mine with Cool Whip instead?" – Kim Kiefer in Redbook

Arg. from Ignorance 5. Title of a pamphlet given out by a religious group: "Can You Prove There is No Hell?"

Circumstantial 6. Aquinas's rational proofs for the existence of God are invalid because he was only trying to justify through reason what he already believed by faith.

Arg from Ignorance 7. There is no such thing as the Abominable Snowman because no one has produced any convincing evidence of him.

Accent 8. DENNIS THE MENACE: The teacher asks Dennis, "How much is 4 and 5, Dennis?" Dennis says, "What do you think, teacher?" The teacher replies, "I don't think...I know!" Dennis says, "I don't think I know, either."

Ad populum 9. Iranian religious leader Ayatullah Ali Khamenei: "Anyone who fights America's aggression has engaged in a holy war in the cause of Allah, and anyone who is killed on that path is a martyr."

Complex Question 10. Our daughter maintained her pencil slim figure until her mid-40s, when she suddenly noticed she had gained some weight. Looking in the mirror, she asked her husband, "Joe, do you think I look fat?"… – Sarah Moore, Athens, Ga.

False dilemma 11. Either the universe has always existed, or it was created by someone who has always existed.

Appeal to authority 12. "My car mechanic says the best way to fix computer problems is to just give the computer a good, sharp kick."

Irrelevant conclusion 13. These antacids cost twice as much as the brand you use, but they are worth it. Each tablet dissolves 50% more acid.

Equivocation 14. One businessman asked another, "Is your advertising getting results?" "It sure is," replied his colleague. "Last week we advertised for a night watchman. The next night we were robbed." – Paul Harwitz in The Wall Street Journal

No Fallacy 15. Stephen Jay Gould, a famous paleontologist, maintains that the dinosaurs were killed by an asteroid that crashed into the earth. I think he is probably right.

Appeal to force 16. CEO: "All employees should make a donation to the American Cancer Society. Show your appreciation that you are presently in a position to be charitable."

Division 17. The German-speaking world has produced the greatest composers: Bach, Handel, Haydn, Mozart, Beethoven, Schubert, Schumann, Brahms, Wagner, Strauss. So the new musical composition of P.J., who is from the German-speaking world, must be among the very best.

False Cause 18. I have tried everything to cure my cold: extra vitamin C, mega doses of other vitamins, Echinacea, but the only thing that seems to help me is black elderberry syrup.

Two wrongs make right 19. Why are you telling me to buy a small, fuel-efficient Honda when you are driving that gas guzzling limousine?

Hasty Generaliz 20. The drug bill that Congress recently passed was written by the pharmaceutical industry. Then energy bill was written by the oil companies. It seems that all politicians have been bought out by big business.

Accident 21. Teachers are supposed to encourage students to succeed. But giving low grades only discourages students.

Exercise 29

Determine whether the following sentences are examples of necessarily true, necessarily false, or empirical sentences.

1. Margaret Mitchell wrote *Gone With the Wind*.
2. A proton is a negatively charged particle.
3. "Roses are red; violets are blue".
4. George Washington was married.
5. George Washington was either married or he was not married.
6. *Look Homeward Angel* was and was not written by Thomas Wolfe.
7. The Empire State Building is in New York City.
8. "A rose is a rose is a rose." - Gertrude Stein
9. A cantata is a composition played solely by musical instruments.

Exercise 30

DIRECTIONS: Specify the premises and conclusions of the following arguments and determine whether they are deductive or inductive. State the reason why you believe the arguments to be deductive or inductive.

1. Mary's mother grows roses. As an experiment, her mother used fertilizer on the roses in the front yard but no fertilizer on a similar-sized plot of roses in the back yard. The front yard yielded twice the number of roses than the back-yard plot. Mary's mother attributed the increase yield to the fertilizer.

2. LAWYER ARGUING IN COURT: It is impossible for William to have seen the reflection of the murderer's face in the glass protecting the painting. All the paintings in that room are oils; glass is used only on watercolors. So William is not telling the truth.

3. There are good reasons against allowing the televised broadcasts of court proceedings. The presence of cameras may waste the time of the judge who must make rulings on their presence, disrupt the trial, distract the jury, and intimidate the witnesses. A trial should not be turned into a circus.

4. Certain people have natural immunity to AIDS because they lack the CCR5 gene. One such person, living in Berlin, donated some of his blood stem cells to an AIDS patient with leukemia. Four years later, the patient appears to be cured of both AIDS and leukemia. Since finding donors is difficult, researchers wanted to discover if they could use the patient's own cells. They took T-cells from six AIDS patients and (by means of genetic engineering) for the first time eliminated a human gene, the CCR5 gene. Then they injected the cells back into the patients. Three months later, in five of the six patients, they found that the altered cells were not only still alive but were also increasing. Researchers hope that if you take away the cells the virus can attack, you may be able to cure the disease.

5. On March 11, 2011 Japan suffered an earthquake that measured 9.0 on the Richter scale, releasing thirty times the energy of the 1906 San Francisco earthquake (that was 7.9). The cooling system failed in several of the Japanese nuclear plants, causing a release of dangerous radiation into the atmosphere. The radiation reached Pacific Coast of the United States in seven days via the jet stream. Just as the island of Japan is riddled with earthquake faults, the same is true of many areas in the United States. Therefore, it is unwise to construct nuclear plants in areas with known earthquake faults.

6. Betty's mother was a great cook. Her specialty was candied yams. This Thanksgiving Betty plans to make some candied yams according to her mother's recipe. So I'm sure they will be delicious.

7. LAWYER ARGUING IN COURT: The house is situated on the keys with the front entrance by the street and the rear entrance by the dock. The murderer could not have entered the house from the front because the painters were working in front all day. They testified that they saw no one enter the house. So the murderer must have arrived by boat and entered the house through the rear. └─→ Amityville horror

8. When interest rates go up, it becomes harder to get a mortgage with a reasonable monthly payment. So as demand slackens, the price of real estate goes down. Therefore, when interest rates rise, the price of real estate will decline.

9. Whenever I had a Icon electric shaver, it always worked well and lasted for a long time. Since I need a shaver now, I am going to buy an Icon because I am sure it is an extremely high quality product.

Exercise 31

DIRECTIONS: Decide which probability law applies, write the law on a piece of paper, then add the numerical probabilities in order to answer the question.

1. What is the probability of drawing either an ace or a jack from a deck of cards on a single draw?

2. What is the probability of getting tails on all three successive tosses of a coin?

3. What is the probability of drawing two kings from a deck of cards in two draws if the first card is not replaced before the second is drawn?

4. What is the probability of drawing at least one king from a deck of cards on two draws if the first card is replaced before the second is drawn?

5. What is the probability of drawing at least one ace from a deck of cards on two draws (if the first card is not replaced before the second is drawn)?

6. What is the probability of drawing three queens from a deck of cards in three draws if the cards are not replaced. Set up the formula with the probabilities. (Don't bother to work out the math.)

7. What is the probability of getting tails at least once in three tosses of a coin?

8. Three cards will be drawn from a deck without replacement. What is the probability that at least one will be an ace? Set up the formula with the probabilities. (Don't bother to work out the math.)

9. What is the probability of rolling a two on a single roll of a die? What are the odds for this event?

10. If the standard odds are 8 to 5 that the Yankees will beat the Dodgers, what is the probability that this event will happen?

Exercise 32

Identify and explain any fallacies.

Division

1. Salt is not a poison. Therefore salt's components (sodium and chloride) must be non-poisonous too.

Against the Person-Abusive

2. Hobo Harry says that we need more welfare programs to help the poor and the dispossessed. But how can you trust the word of a lazy bum who hasn't done an honest day's work his whole life?

Amphiboly

3. I am much too shy to go to the laundromat. It has a sign that says, "Customers Must Remove All Clothing as Soon as the Machine Stops."

Against the Person- Circumstantial

4. This rent control bill is intrusive and socialistic. As you might suspect, only renters support it.

Appeal to Authority

5. "But can you doubt that air has weight when you have the clear testimony of Aristotle affirming that all the elements have weight including air, and excepting only fire?" (Galileo, *Dialogues Concerning Two New Sciences*.)

Appeal to force

6. "Ladies and gentlemen of the jury, if you do not convict this murderer, you may end up his next victim."

Two wrongs Make a right

7. FATHER: At your age Franklin D. Roosevelt was Assistant Secretary of the Navy; you're nothing but a college drop out.
SON: At your age Franklin D. Roosevelt was president. He was not living on unemployment like you are.

Hasty Gen

8. "In Philadelphia nearly everyone reads the <u>Bulletin</u>".

9. At a trial to determine if Bertrand Russell should be allowed to teach philosophy of mathematics at New York City College, the prosecution argued: "Russell conducted a nudist colony in England. His children paraded nude. He and his wife have paraded nude in public. This man who is now about seventy has gone in for salacious poetry. Russell winks at homosexuality. I'd go further and say he approves of it."

Accident

10. "We're worried about your son, Mr. Astor," says the ninth-grade teacher. "He seems very manipulative. He convinces Bobby to do all his work for him." "Manipulative!" exclaims Mr. Astor, "That's executive ability."